MW00395679

TAGALOG

Activities for Kids

My Family and Home

Ang Pamilya at Tahanan ko

Ang aklat ni (This book belongs to):

Contents

Text Copyright © 2023 by Bien-Elize C. Roque-Nido
Illustrations Copyright © 2023 by Stephanie Castillo Braulio

All rights reserved. This book or any portion thereof may not be reproduced or used in any manner whatsoever without the express written permission of the publisher, except for the use of brief quotations in a book review.

Book Design by McKenly Santos
Edited by Dianne Que

Printed in the United States of America.

First Printing, 2023

ISBN 978-1-7341241-4-9

Wonderbred Press
www.wonderbred.co

Para sa aming mga ninuno

About Tagalog Activities for Kids

This bilingual workbook series is inspired by our own childhood Tagalog-learning experiences (or lack thereof) as children of Philippine immigrants in the States.

Growing up, some of us were gently steered away from the language and traditions of our motherland, for a number of reasons. Fast forward to now, and we, as parents ourselves, are taking a different approach. Our mission is to reconnect with our heritage and propagate Philippine culture through the learning tools we create for future generations.

So, while much has been written about the benefits of early bilingual language learning–improved cognitive development, mental flexibility, increased empathy, and so on–we especially value the bonds it can build between children and their ancestors.

Happy learning! Maligayang pag-aaral (ma-li-GA-yang pag-a-A-ral)!

How to get the most out of this book

1. Chapters are split into two parts, each beginning with a picture glossary page. Bookmark these and use them as your reference!

2. Read each Tagalog word aloud while pointing at the corresponding pictures or the objects/people in real life. Review words again after completing activities.

3. Incorporate newly learned Tagalog vocabulary into your daily routines at home.

Phonetics

At this level, we keep things simple, focusing mostly on meaning and offering just a bit of help with pronunciation. For instance, we have indicated which syllables should be EM-phasized, and have sprinkled in some reminders for how to say Tagalog vowels:

A-E-I-O-U should be pronounced *AH-EH-EE-OH-OO* (like in Spanish)

Our Secret Sawsawan

Our language-learning "sauce" may not actually be a secret, but it is by our own design, and it's informed by actual teaching theories. With that in mind, our approach to early bilingual language development starts with four steps:

Expose
Introduce the sounds and shapes of words. Let children touch, trace, identify them. Foster familiarity, even if it seems superficial at first.

Define
Give meaning to words. Help children understand, visualize, and begin using them.

Classify
Relate words to others. Show children how the words fit within the world around them.

Personalize
Bring words to life. Create personal connections with words to build resonance on a deeper level.

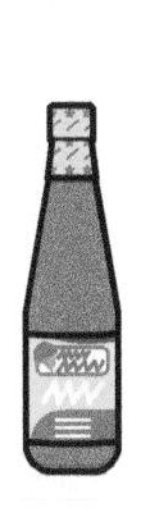

A Note on Tagalog vs. Filipino

Many people (Filipinos and otherwise) use the terms *Tagalog* and *Filipino* interchangeably when referring to the language of the Philippines. While they may not be wrong, there is a bit of nuance between the terms that we think is important to clarify.

The official national language of the Philippines is *Filipino*, which is mostly based on the native Philippine language *Tagalog*, but also incorporates some elements from the country's other 100+ native languages. To add to the confusion, *Filipino* was once called *Pilipino* (but not anymore), and initially, it even used a different alphabet (which had only 20 letters).

Anyway, there's a lot of controversy, politics, and conflict in the history of our country's language(s), so we'll just say that because our parents (and many others') grew up speaking *Tagalog*, our books are intended to teach the beginnings of that language... which, of course, also happen to be the beginnings of *Filipino*. Ay naku!

PART ONE

Ang Pamilya Ko

My Family

Psst! Bookmark this page for easy reference. And remember that Tagalog vowels *A-E-I-O-U* are pronounced *AH-EH-EE-OH-OO*.

anak
(a-NAK)

child

ate
(A-te)

older sister

kuya
(KU-ya)

older brother

lola
(LO-la)

grandmother

lolo
(LO-lo)

grandfather

nanay
(NA-nay)

mother

pamilya
(pa-MIL-ya)

family

tatay
(TA-tay)

father

tita
(TI-ta)

aunt

tito
(TI-to)

uncle

Say the Tagalog words out loud and trace them.

NANAY

LOLA

TATAY

LOLO

ATE

Trace the lines to connect the family members. Talk about how they're related.

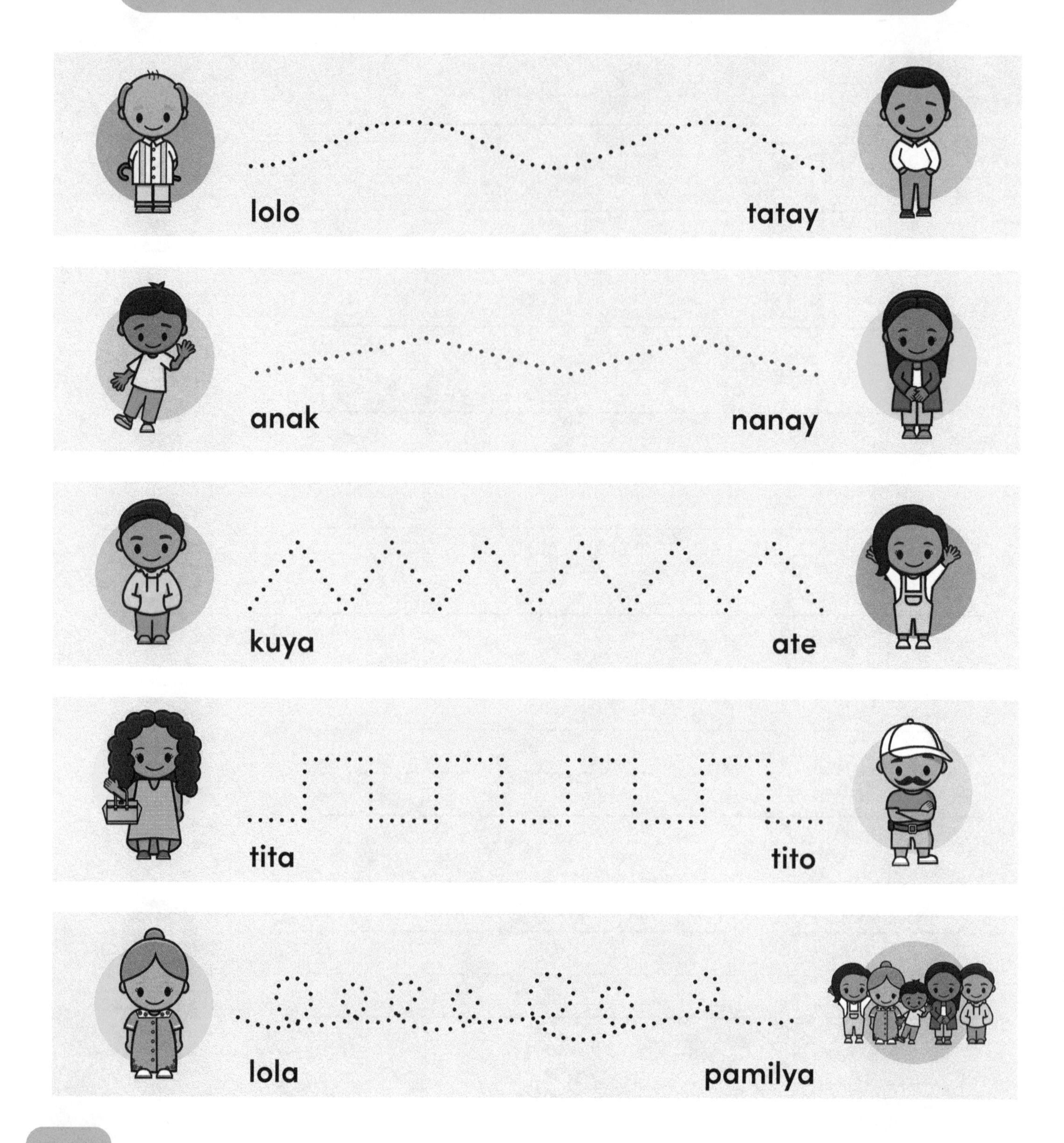

Find and circle the anak.

Circle the pictures that belong in a family.

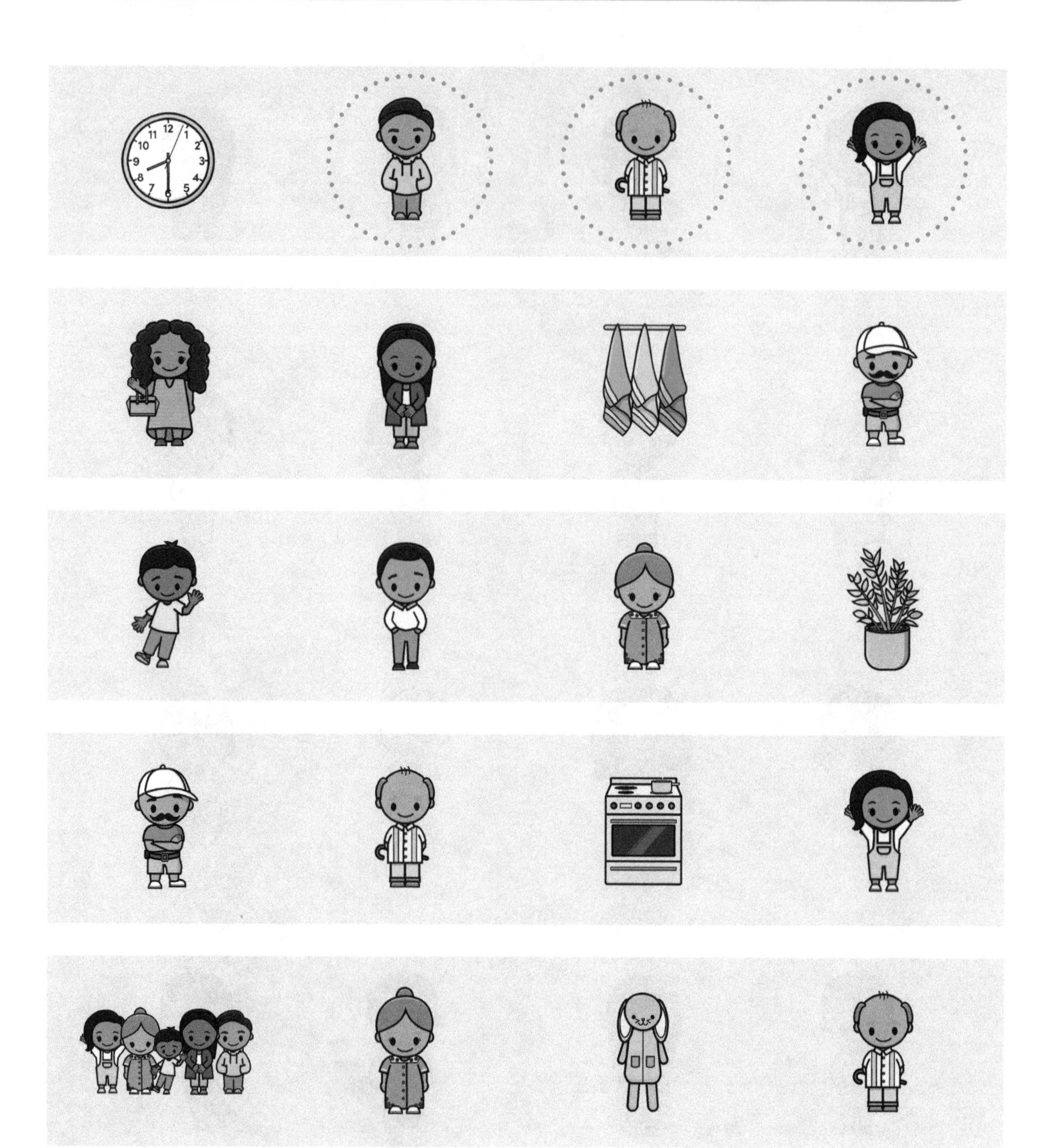

Circle the biggest picture.

Draw yourself.

Complete the activity in each box.

anak
(a-NAK)

Say the word out loud.

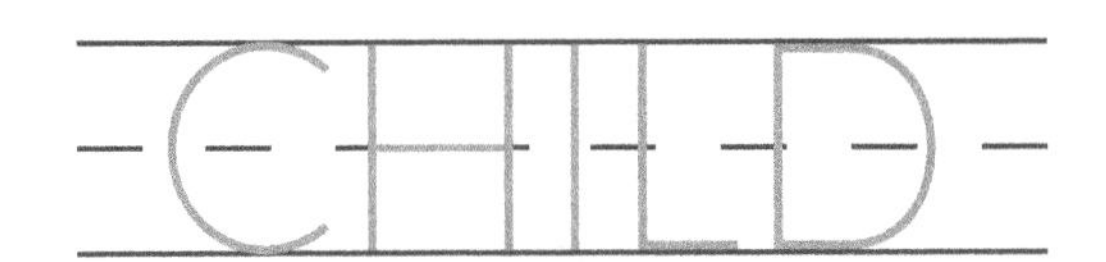

Trace the English word.

Color the anak.

Draw a child.

pamilya
(pa-MIL-ya)

Say the word out loud.

Trace the English word.

Color the pamilya.

Draw a family.

PART TWO

Ang Pamilya Ko

My Family

Psst! Bookmark this page for easy reference. And remember that Tagalog vowels *A-E-I-O-U* are pronounced *AH-EH-EE-OH-OO*.

babae
(ba-BA-e)
woman/girl

bata
(BA-ta)
child/kid

bunso
(bun-SO)
youngest child

kaibigan
(ka-i-BI-gan)
friend

kapatid
(ka-pa-TID)
sibling

lalaki
(la-LA-ki)
man/boy

ninang
(NI-nang)
godmother

ninong
(NI-nong)
godfather

panganay
(pa-NGA-nay)
eldest child

pinsan
(PIN-san)
cousin

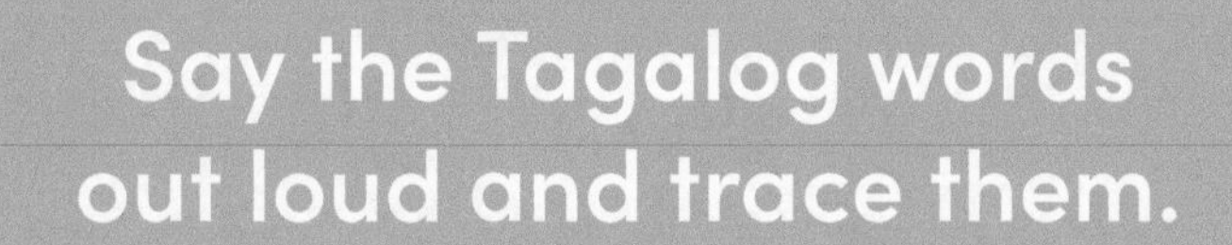

Say the Tagalog words out loud and trace them.

BABAE

BATA

NINANG

LALAKI

NINONG

Say the Tagalog words out loud and trace the missing letters.

KAPATID

PINSAN

PANGANAY

BUNSO

KAIBIGAN

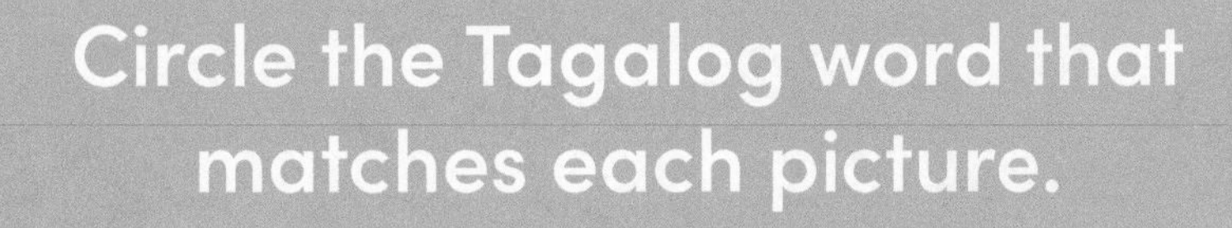

Circle the Tagalog word that matches each picture.

babae

ninang

bunso

godmother

lalaki | bunso | panganay

man

pinsan | bata | ninong

kid

babae | panganay | kaibigan

woman

babae | ninang | ninong

godfather

Draw a line to match the numbers with the correct pictures.

4 babae

3 lalaki

2 bata

3 kaibigan

2 panganay

Circle the picture that continues each pattern.

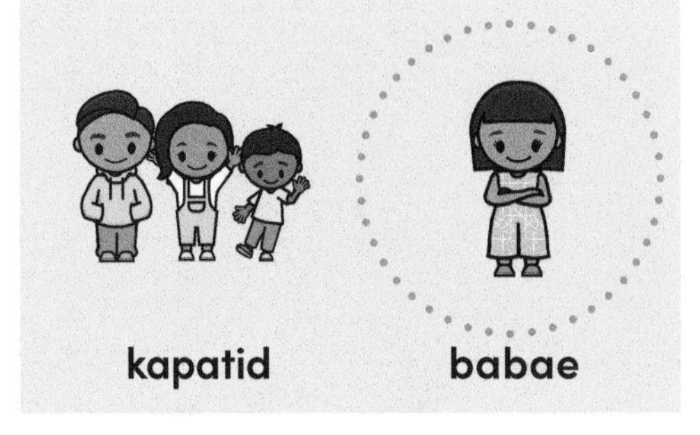

Draw your kaibigan.

Complete the activity in each box.

babae
(ba-BA-e)

Say the word out loud.

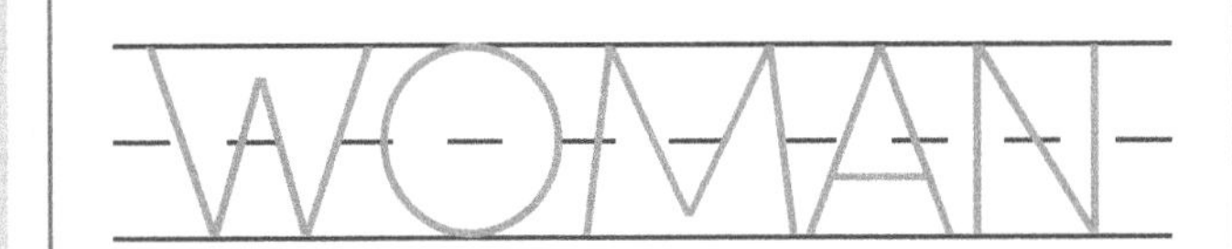

Trace the English word.

Color the picture.

Draw a woman.

pinsan
(PIN-san)

Say the word out loud.

Trace the English word.

Color the picture.

Draw a cousin.

PART ONE

Kusina

Kitchen

Psst! Bookmark this page for easy reference. And remember that Tagalog vowels *A-E-I-O-U* are pronounced *AH-EH-EE-OH-OO*.

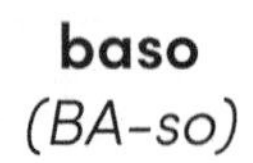

baso
(BA-so)

drinking glass

kalan
(ka-LAN)

stove

kaldero
(kal-DE-ro)

pot

kutsara
(ku-CHA-ra)

spoon

kutsilyo
(ku-CHIL-yo)

knife

lamesa
(la-ME-sa)

table

pinggan
(ping-GAN)

plate

upuan
(u-pu-AN)

chair

tinidor
(ti-ni-DOR)

fork

kusina
(ku-SI-na)

kitchen

Say the Tagalog words out loud and trace the missing letters.

BASO

LAMESA

UPUAN

KALDERO

TINIDOR

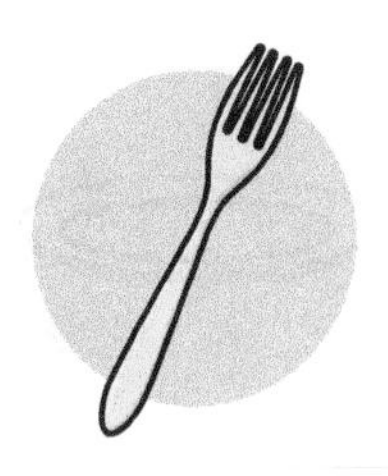

Connect the picture to its matching Tagalog word.

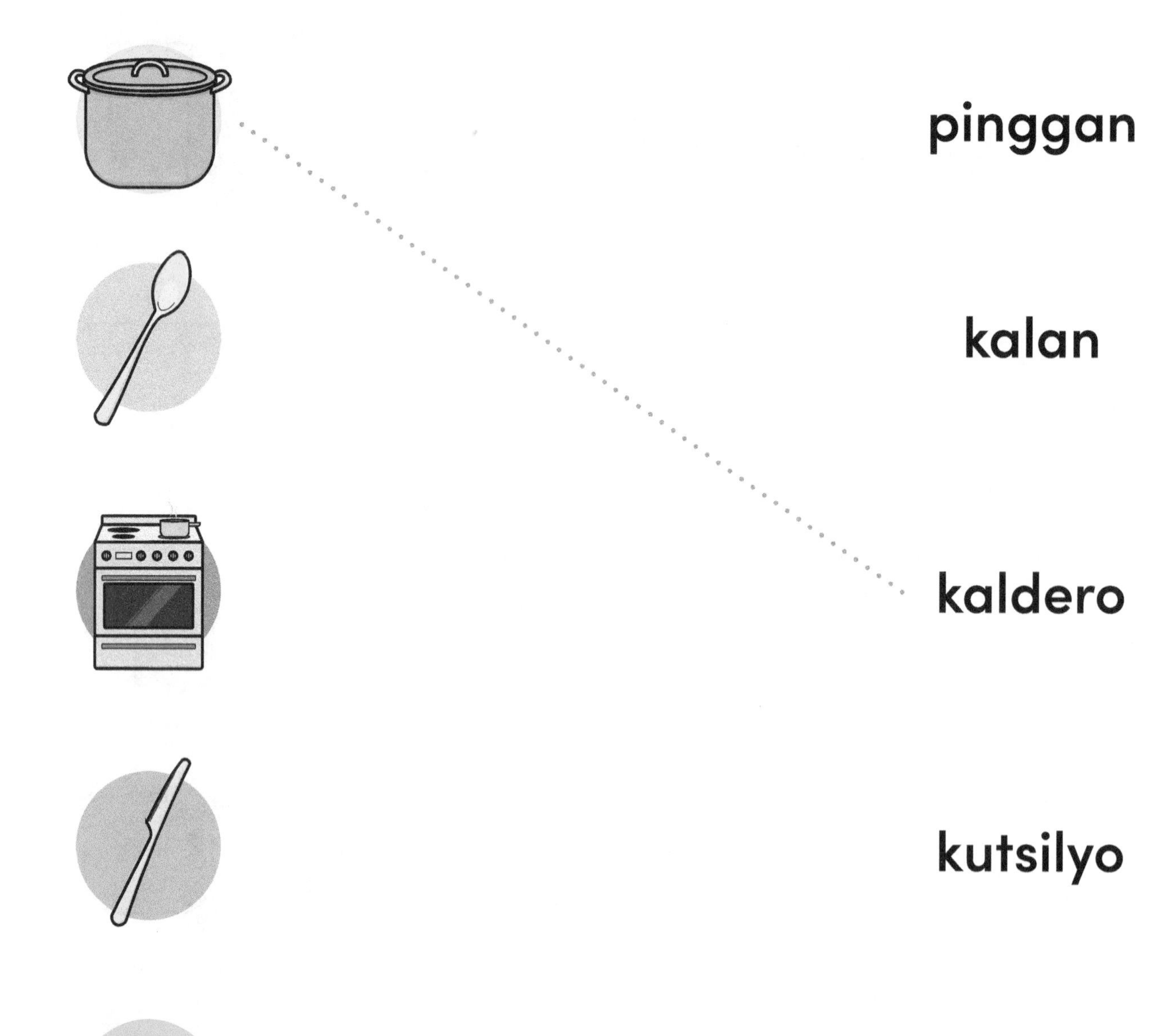

Draw a path to help Lolo find his baso.

Circle the Tagalog word that matches each pitcture.

kutsara tinidor baso

cup

upuan tinidor pinggan

fork

lamesa kalan kusina

stove

kusina lamesa baso

kitchen

upuan pinggan kutsilyo

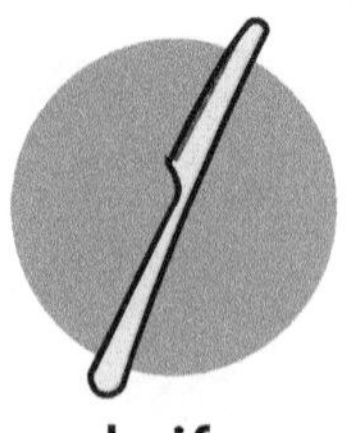

knife

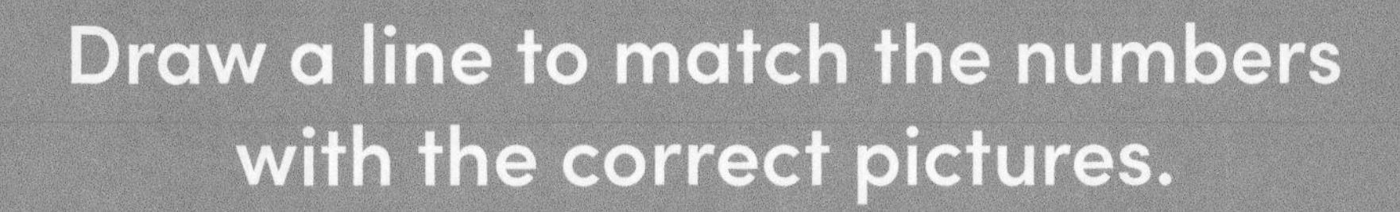
Draw a line to match the numbers
with the correct pictures.

4
upuan

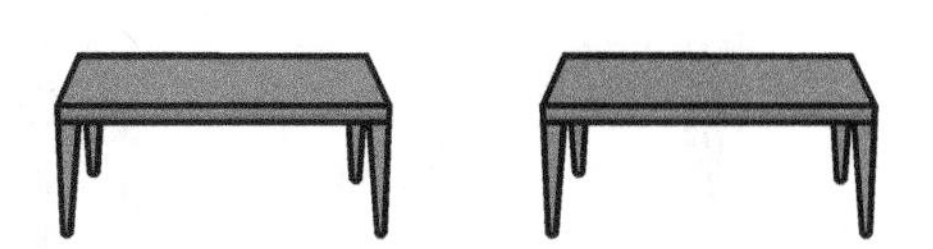

3
baso

2
lamesa

2
kaldero

3
pinggan

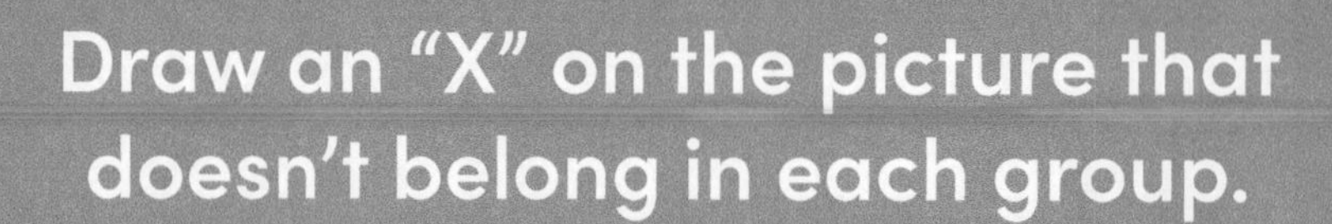

Draw an "X" on the picture that doesn't belong in each group.

Circle the picture that continues each pattern.

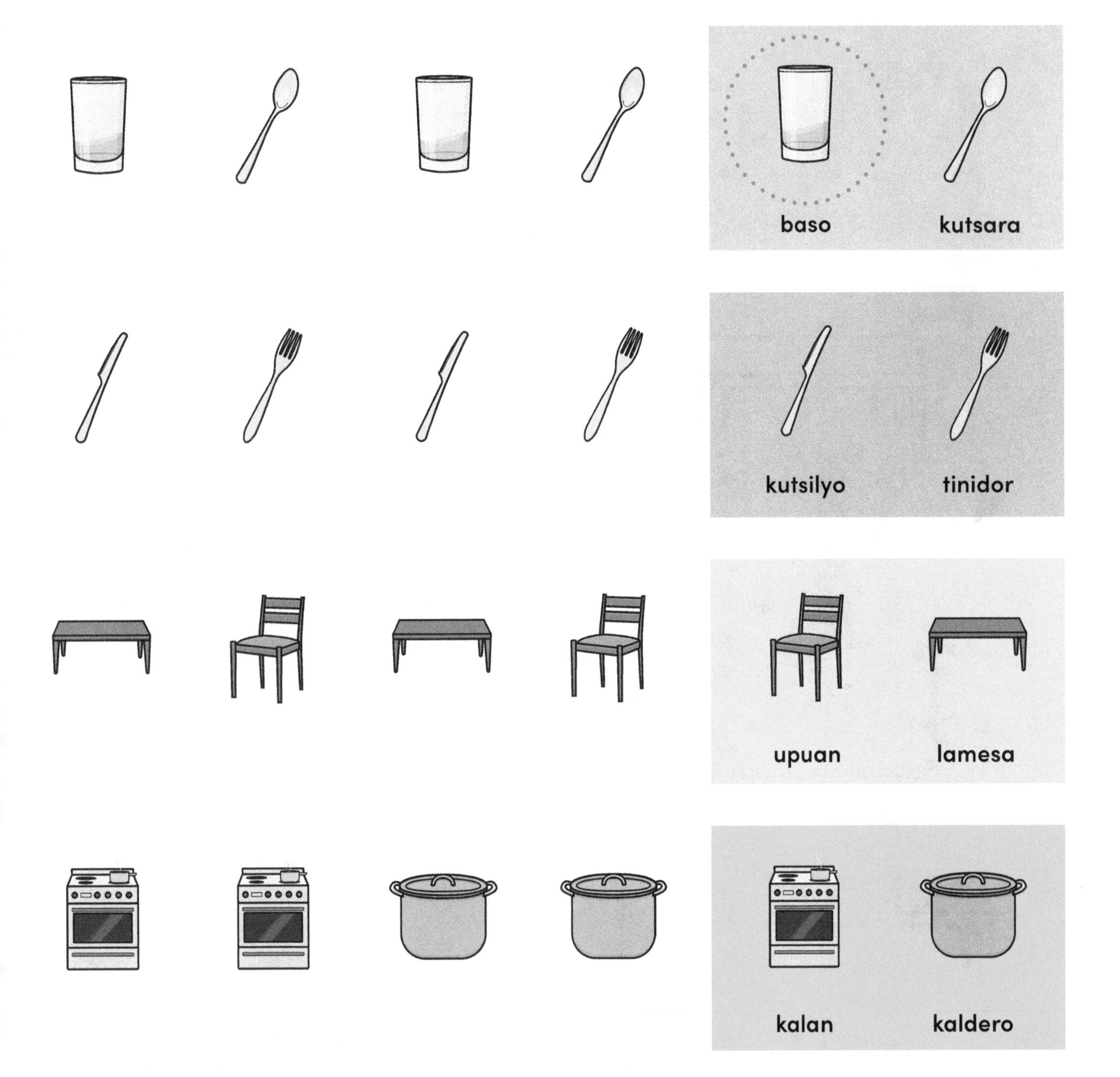

Complete the activity in each box.

lamesa
(la-ME-sa)

Say the word out loud.

Trace the English word.

Color the lamesa.

Draw a table.

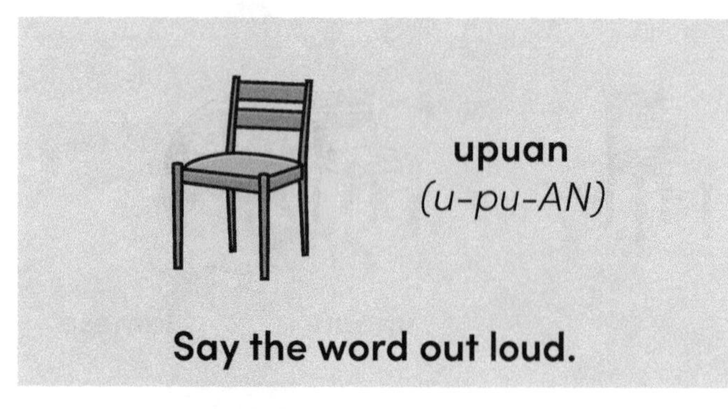

upuan
(u-pu-AN)

Say the word out loud.

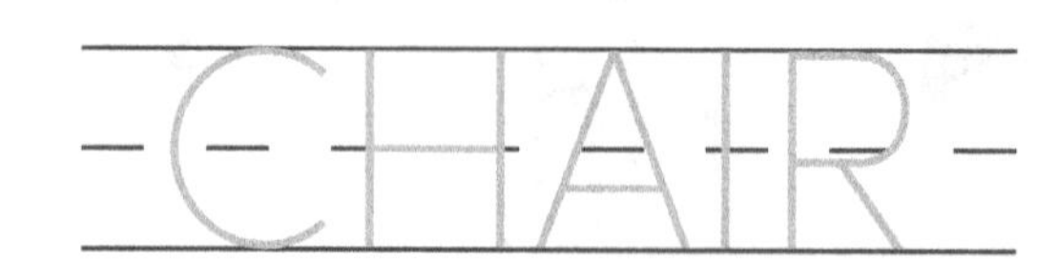

Trace the English word.

Color the upuan.

Draw a chair.

Complete the activity in each box.

pinggan
(ping-GAN)

Say the word out loud.

Trace the English word.

Color the pinggan.

Draw a plate.

baso
(BA-so)

Say the word out loud.

Trace the English word.

Color the baso.

Draw a glass.

PART TWO

Kusina

Kitchen

Psst! Bookmark this page for easy reference. And remember that Tagalog vowels *A-E-I-O-U* are pronounced *AH-EH-EE-OH-OO*.

gripo
(GRI-po)

faucet

pugon
(pu-GON)

oven

kumain
(ku-MA-in)

to eat

magluto
(mag-LU-to)

to cook

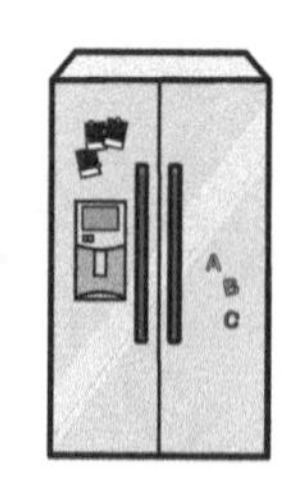

pridyider
(PRI-ji-der)

refrigerator

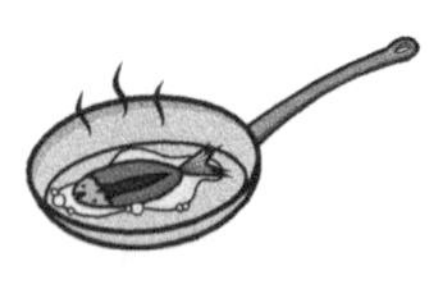

magprito
(mag-PRI-to)

to fry

sandok
(san-DOK)

scoop/ladle

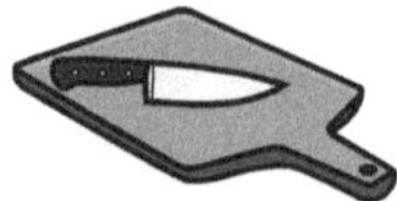

tadtaran
(tad-TA-ran)

cutting board

tasa
(TA-sa)

cup

walis
(wa-LIS)

broom

Say the Tagalog words out loud and trace the missing letters.

MAGPRITO

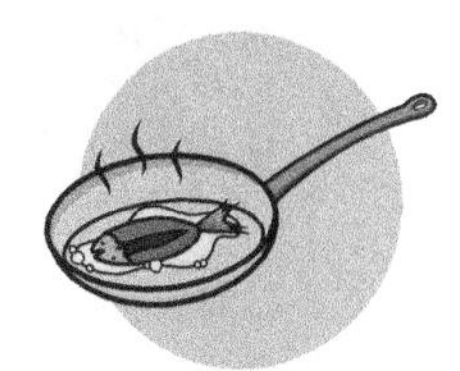

PUGON

SANDOK

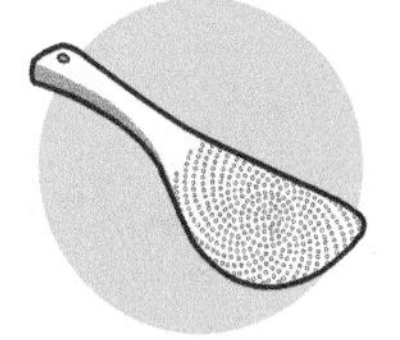

WALIS

GRIPO

Trace the line to connect the Tagalog word to its matching picture.

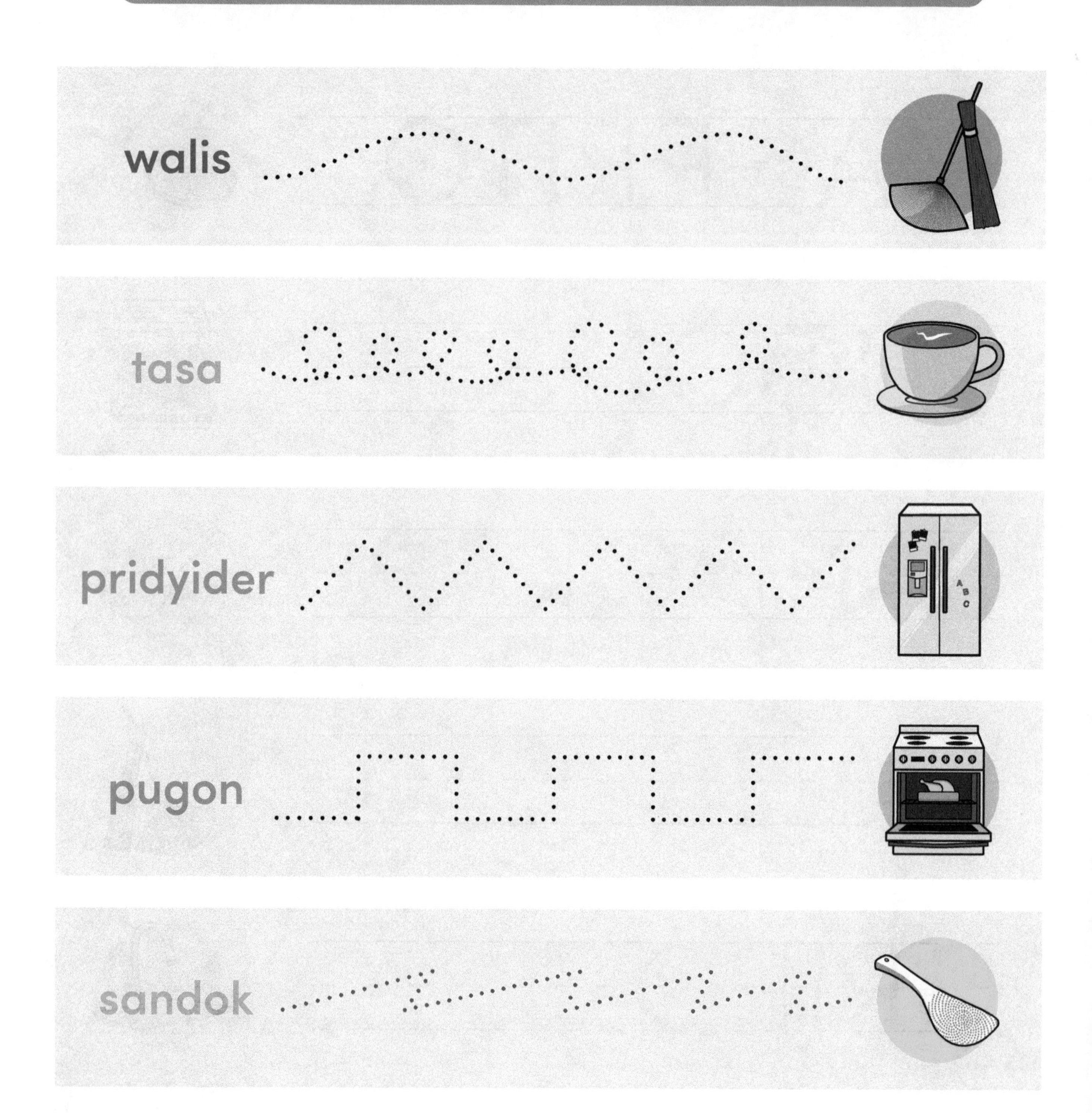

Draw a path to rinse the sandok under the gripo.

Connect the picture to its matching Tagalog word.

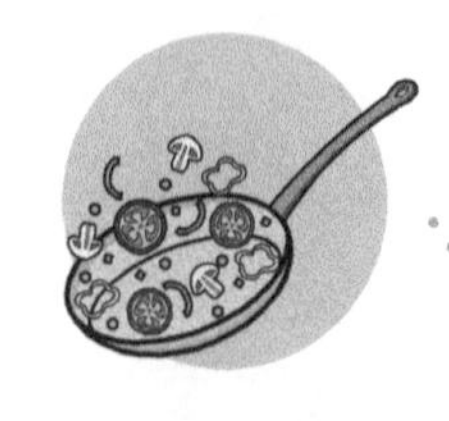

gripo

tadtaran

magprito

kumain

magluto

Draw a line to match the numbers with the correct pictures.

3
pugon

2
pridyider

2
walis

4
tasa

3
gripo

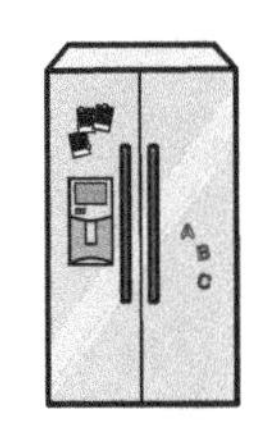
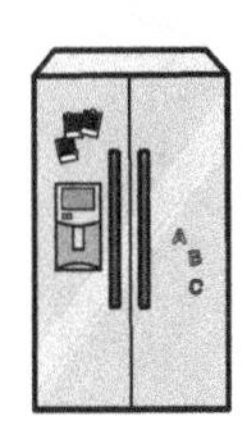

Circle the Tagalog word that matches each picture.

sandok  walis gripo

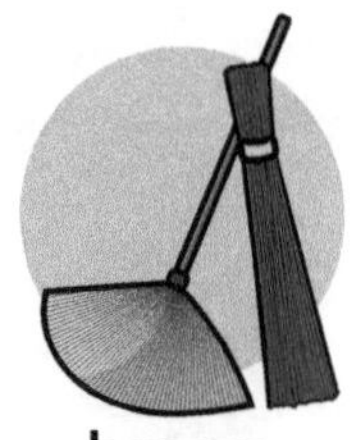

broom

pridyider tasa magluto

refrigerator

magprito sandok pugon

oven

tadtaran tasa walis

cup

gripo kumain magluto

faucet

Draw an "X" on the picture that doesn't belong in each group.

Complete the activity in each box.

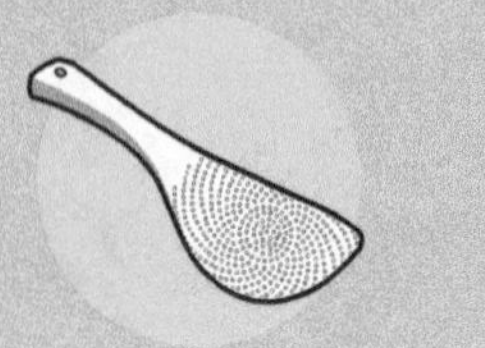

sandok
(san-DOK)

Say the word out loud.

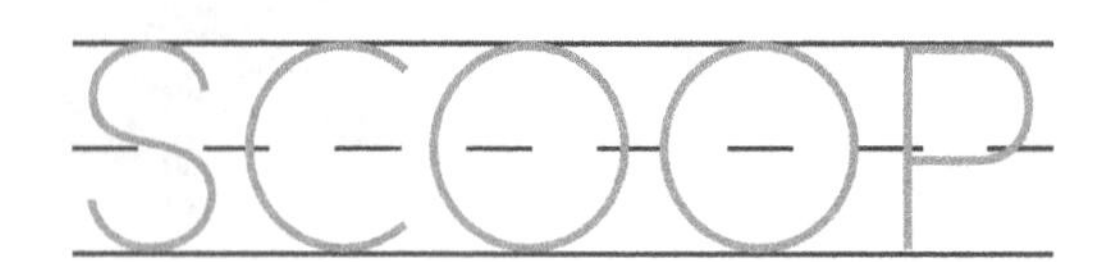

Trace the English word.

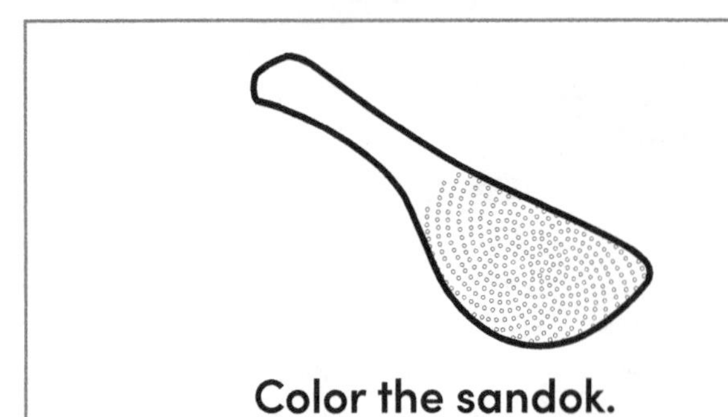

Color the sandok.

Draw a scoop/ladle.

tasa
(TA-sa)

Say the word out loud.

Trace the English word.

Color the tasa.

Draw a cup.

Complete the activity in each box.

kumain
(ku-MA-in)

Say the word out loud.

Trace the English word.

Color the picture.

Draw yourself eating.

magluto
(mag-LU-to)

Say the word out loud.

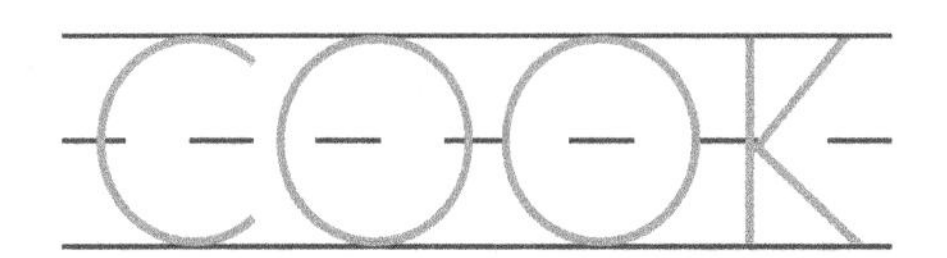

Trace the English word.

Color the picture.

Draw someone cooking.

PART ONE

Sala

Living Room

Psst! Bookmark this page for easy reference. And remember that Tagalog vowels *A-E-I-O-U* are pronounced *AH-EH-EE-OH-OO*.

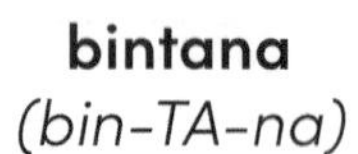

bintana
(bin-TA-na)

window

dingding
(ding-DING)

wall

halaman
(ha-LA-man)

plant

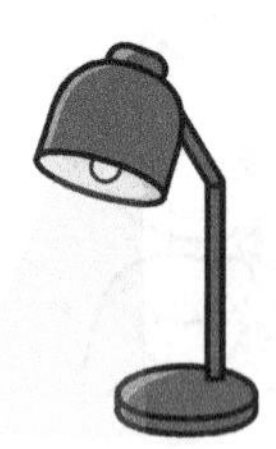

ilaw
(I-law)

light

larawan
(la-RA-wan)

picture

laruan
(la-ru-AN)

toy

orasan
(or-a-SAN)

clock

sahig
(sa-HIG)

floor

sala
(SA-la)

living room

upuan
(u-pu-AN)

chair

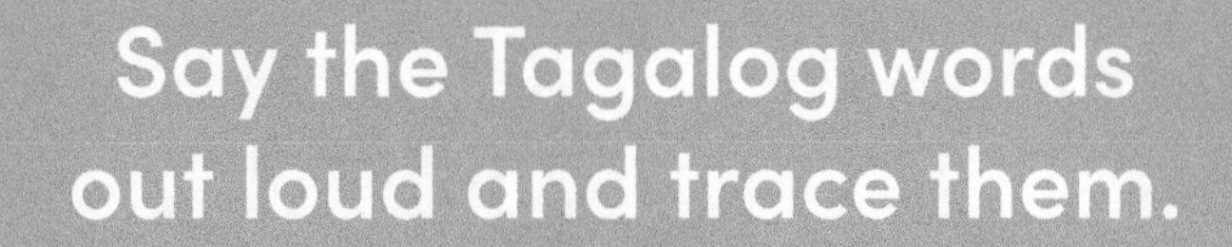

Say the Tagalog words out loud and trace them.

UPUAN

HALAMAN

DINGDING

BINTANA

LARUAN

Connect the picture to its matching Tagalog word.

halaman

sahig

bintana

larawan

ilaw

Circle the Tagalog word that matches each picture.

orasan  upuan sala

chair

ilaw halaman larawan

light

sahig bintana halaman

plant

larawan ilaw orasan

clock

bintana sala sahig

living room

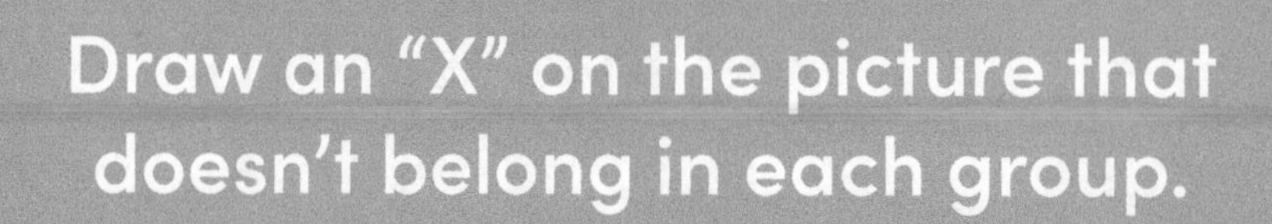

Draw an "X" on the picture that doesn't belong in each group.

Circle the number of items in each group.

Sala
(SA-la)

Say the word out loud.

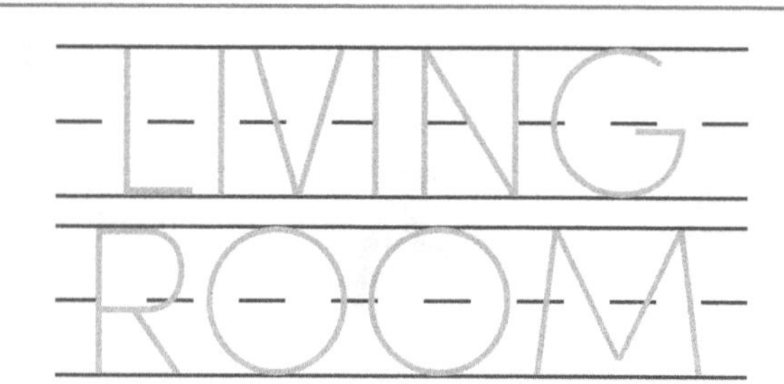

Trace the English word.

Color the sala.

Draw a living room.

halaman
(ha-LA-man)

Say the word out loud.

Trace the English word.

Color the halaman.

Draw a plant.

Complete the activity in each box.

laruan
(la-ru-AN)

Say the word out loud.

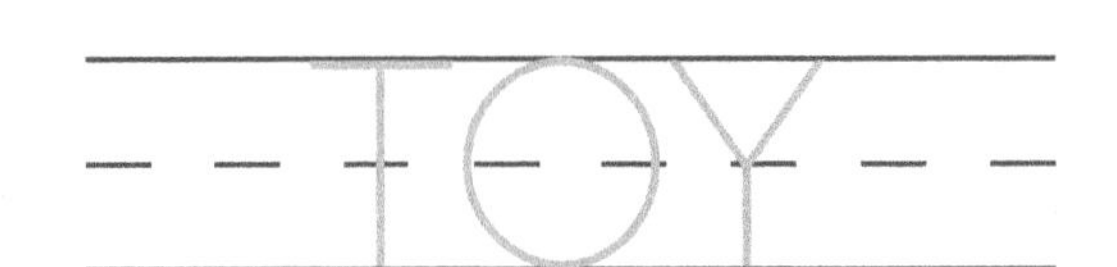

Trace the English word.

Color the laruan.

Draw a toy.

orasan
(or-a-SAN)

Say the word out loud.

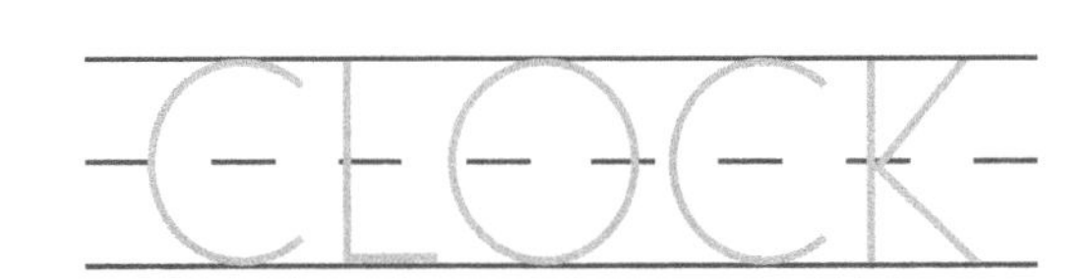

Trace the English word.

Color the orasan.

Draw a clock.

PART TWO

Sala

Living Room

Psst! Bookmark this page for easy reference. And remember that Tagalog vowels *A-E-I-O-U* are pronounced *AH-EH-EE-OH-OO*.

bentilador
(ben-ti-la-DOR)

electric fan

hagdanan
(hag-DA-nan)

stairs

maglaro
(mag-la-RO)

to play

makinig
(ma-ki-NIG)

to listen

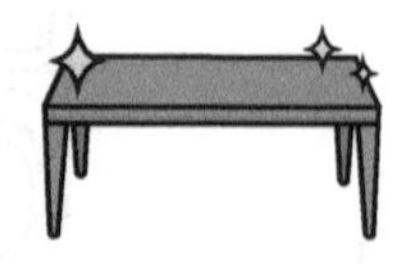

malinis
(ma-LI-nis)

clean

manood
(ma-no-OD)

to watch

radyo
(RA-jo)

radio

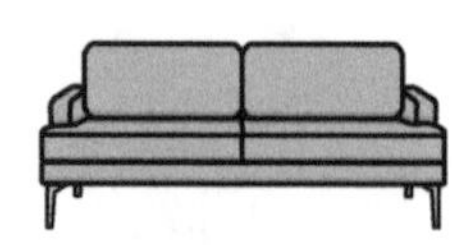

supa
(su-PA)

couch

umupo
(um-u-PO)

to sit

telebisyon
(te-le-bis-YON)

television

Say the Tagalog words out loud and trace them.

RADYO

BENTILADOR

MAKINIG

SUPA

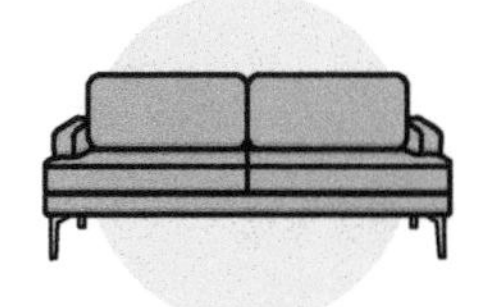

HAGDANAN

Draw a path from the supa
to the telebisyon.

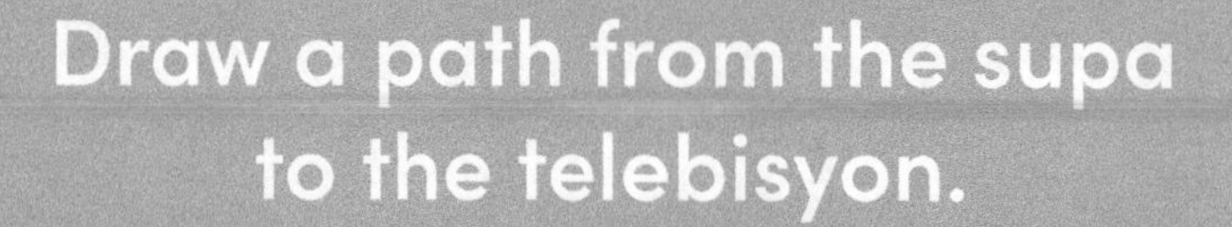

Trace the line to connect the Tagalog word to its matching picture.

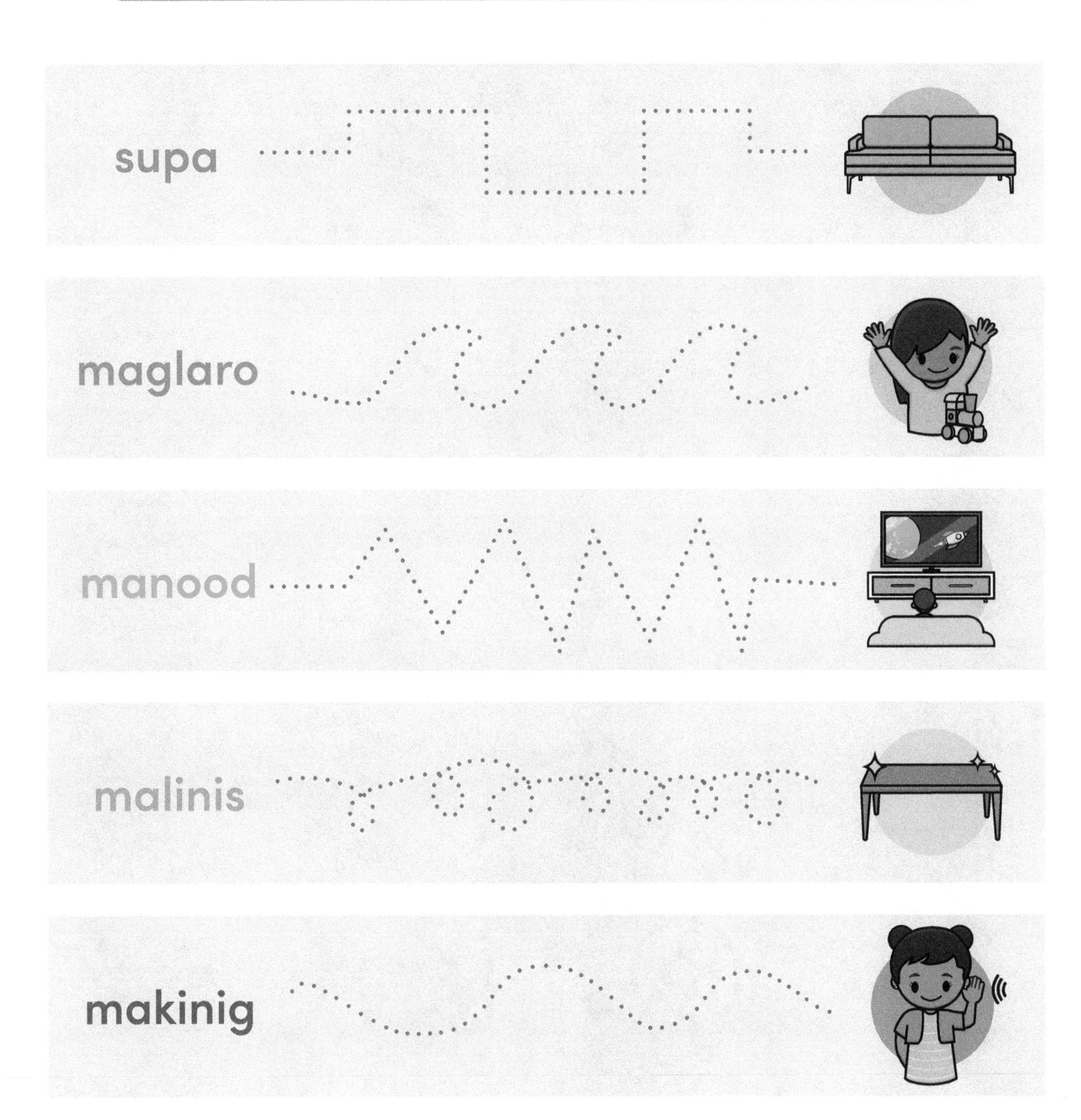

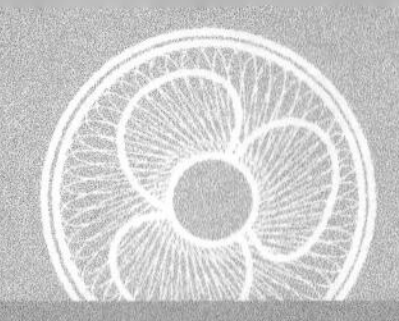

Trace the line to connect the Tagalog word to its matching picture.

umupo

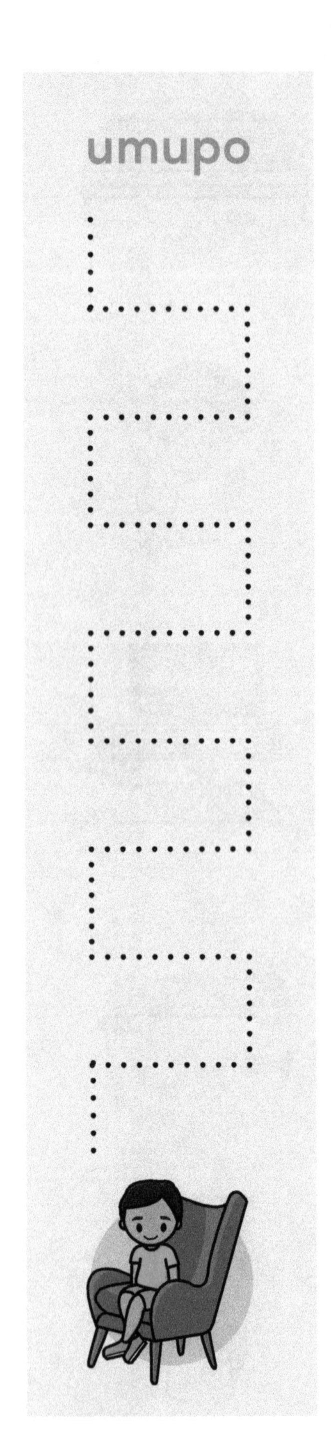

bentilador

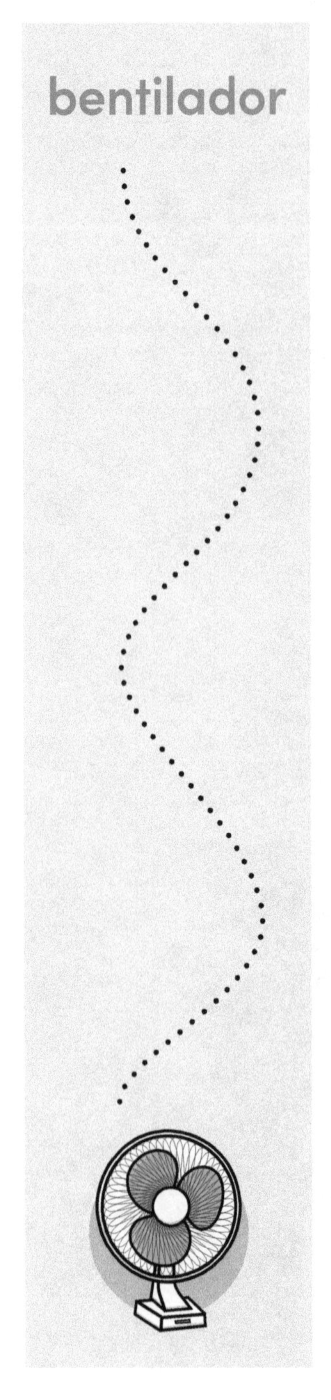

telebisyon

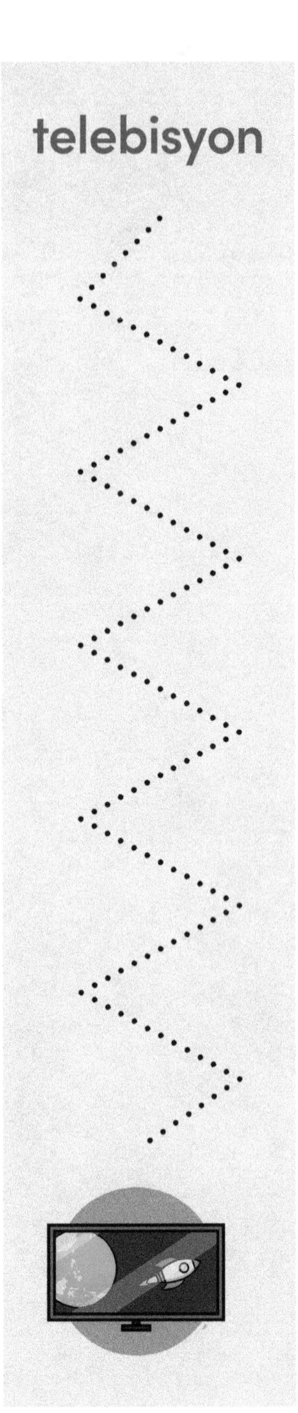

radyo

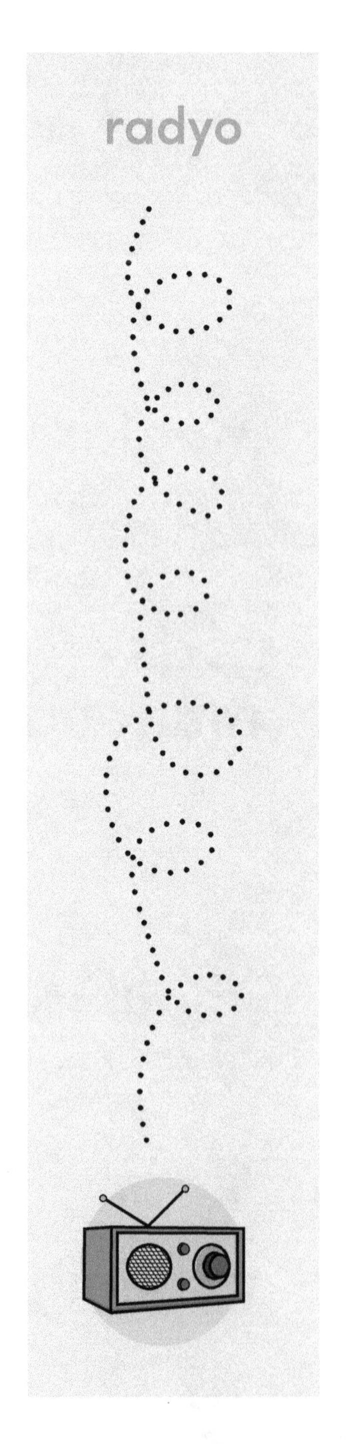

Circle the biggest picture. Say the name of the picture in Tagalog.

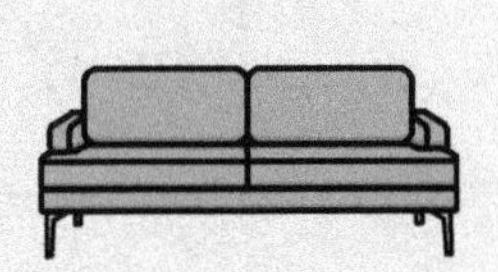
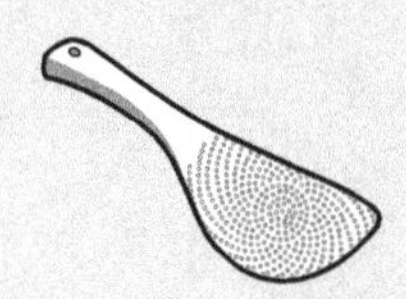
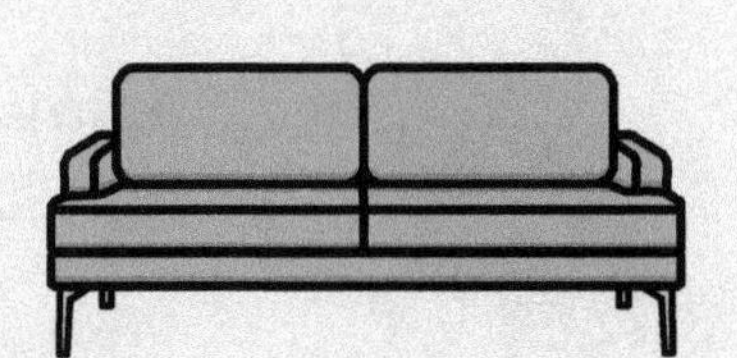

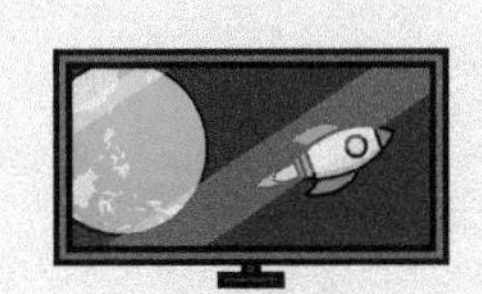

Complete the activity in each box.

umupo
(um-u-PO)

Say the word out loud.

Trace the English word.

Color the picture.

Draw yourself sitting down.

maglaro
(mag-la-RO)

Say the word out loud.

Trace the English word.

Color the picture.

Draw yourself playing.

Complete the activity in each box.

manood
(ma-no-OD)

Say the word out loud.

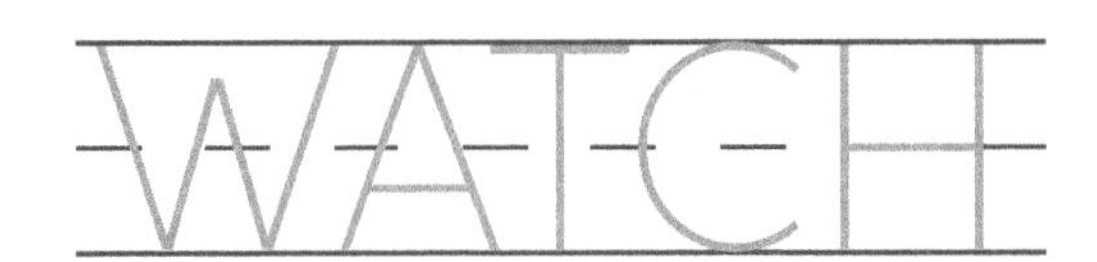

Trace the English word.

Color the picture.

Draw yourself watching TV.

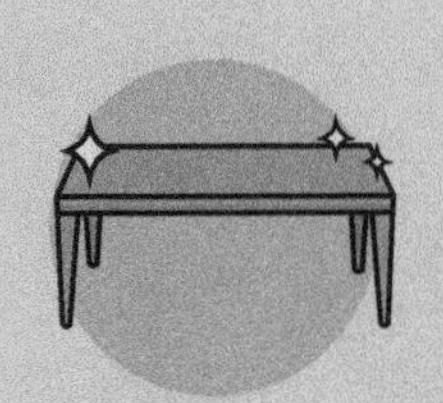

malinis
(ma-LI-nis)

Say the word out loud.

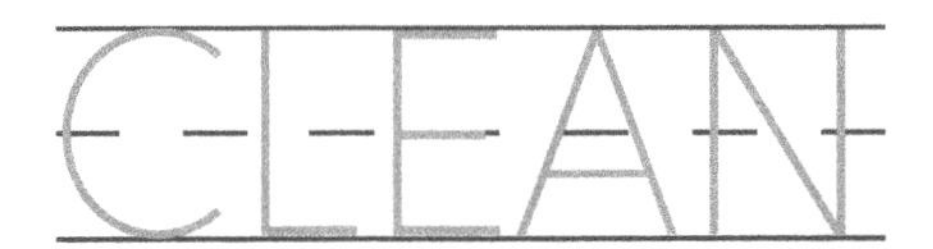

Trace the English word.

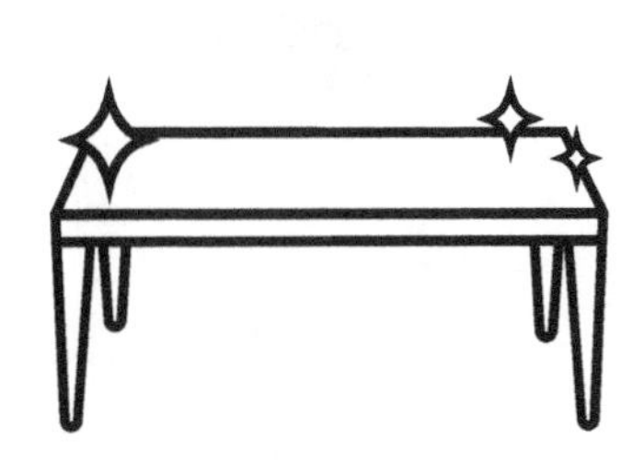

Color the picture.

Draw a clean table.

PART ONE

Kuwarto

Bedroom

Psst! Bookmark this page for easy reference. And remember that Tagalog vowels *A-E-I-O-U* are pronounced *AH-EH-EE-OH-OO*.

aklat
(ak-LAT)
book

aparador
(a-pa-ra-DOR)
closet

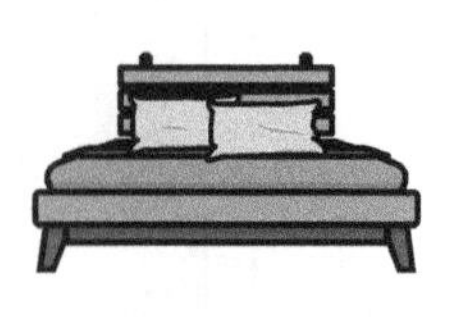

kama
(KA-ma)
bed

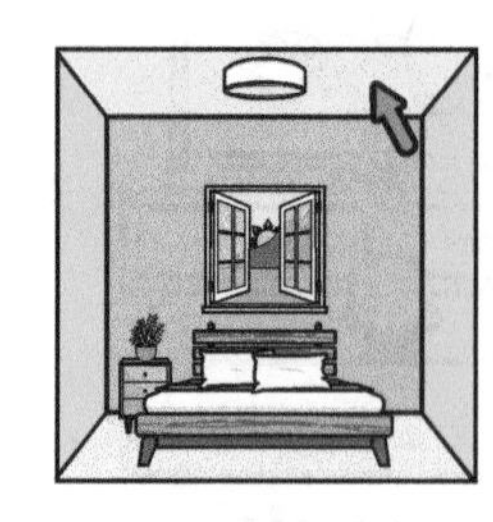

kisame
(KI-sa-me)
ceiling

kumot
(KU-mot)
blanket

kuwarto
(KWAR-to)
bedroom

manika
(ma-NI-ka)
doll

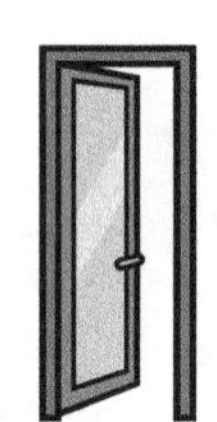

pinto
(pin-TO)
door

tokador
(to-ka-DOR)
dresser

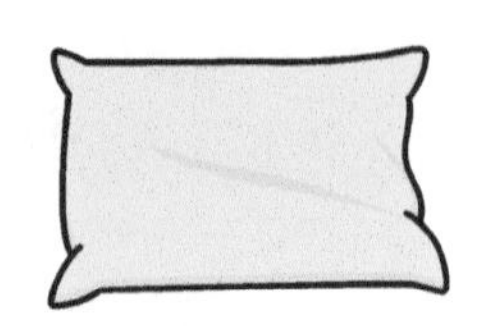

unan
(U-nan)
pillow

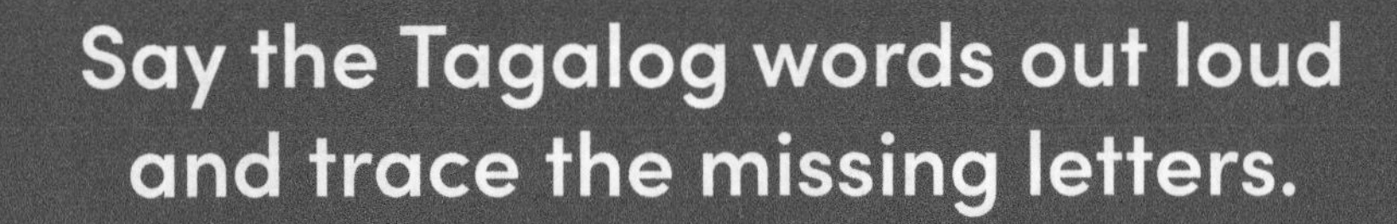

PINTO

KAMA

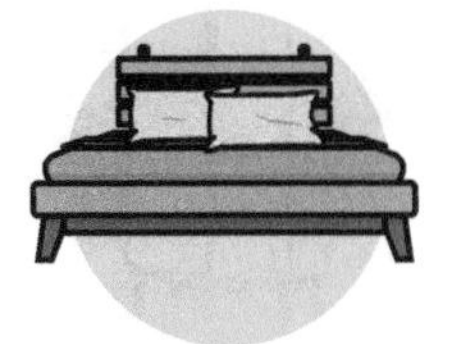

UNAN

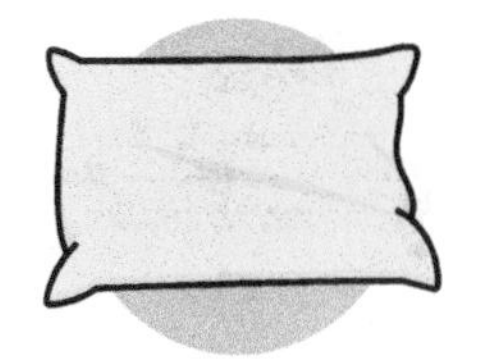

MANIKA

KUMOT

Connect the picture to its matching Tagalog word.

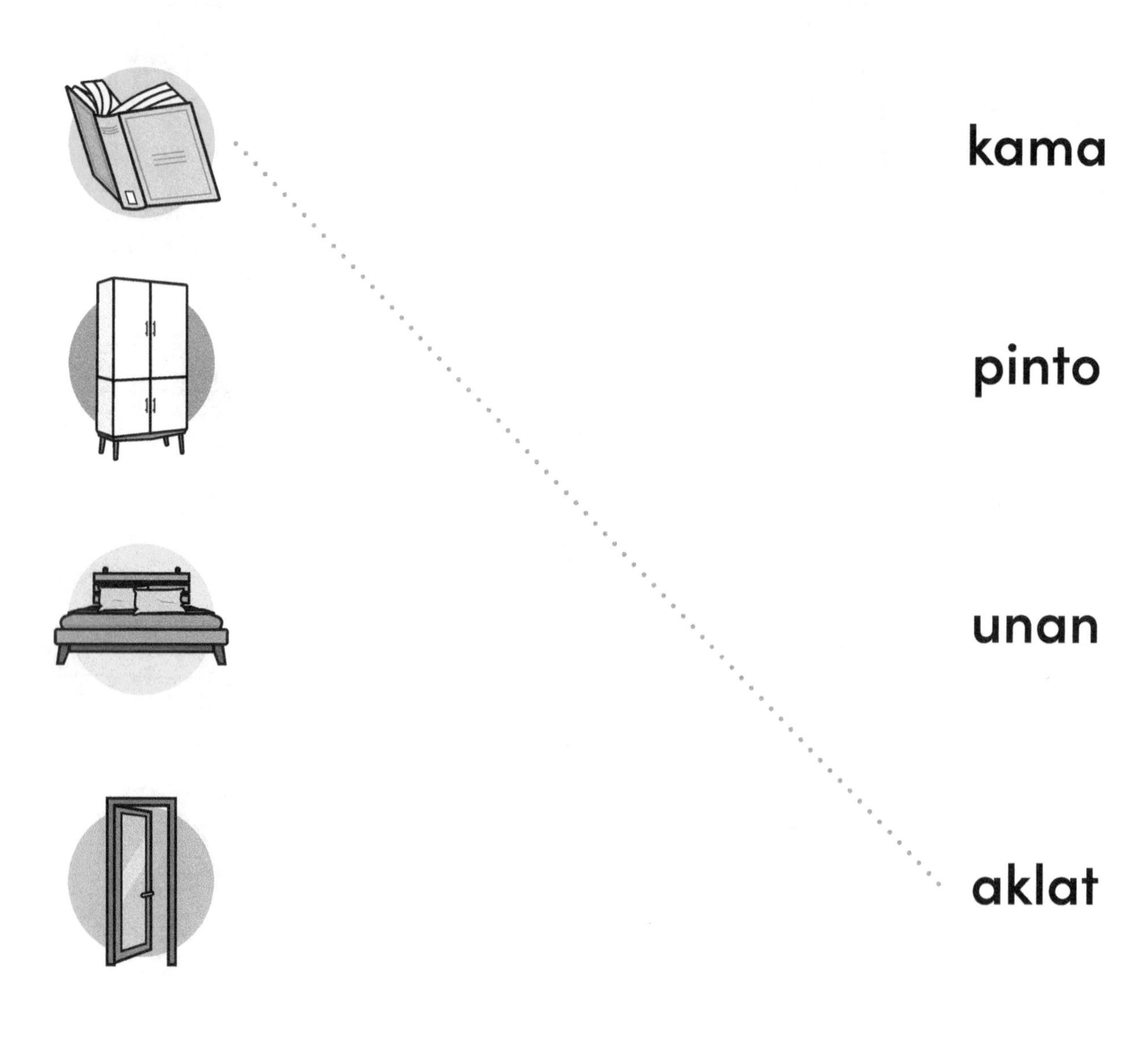

Circle the Tagalog word that matches each picture.

pinto manika  kama

bed

unan aklat kumot

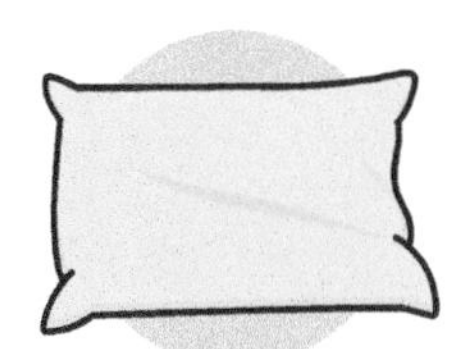

pillow

kuwarto kumot tokador

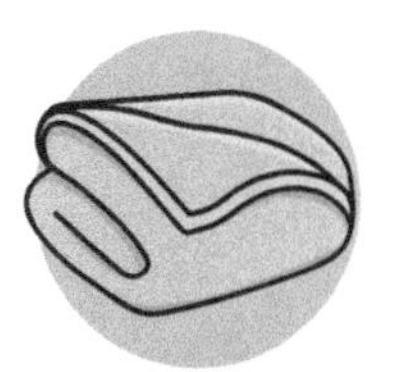

blanket

tokador kuwarto kama

bedroom

aklat aparador pinto

book

Circle the Tagalog word that matches each picture.

tokador  aparador unan

closet

kisame tokador pinto

dresser

aklat kumot manika

doll

pinto kuwarto unan

door

aklat kumot kisame

ceiling

Circle the picture that continues each pattern.

 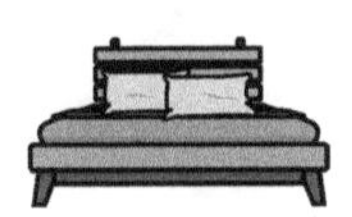  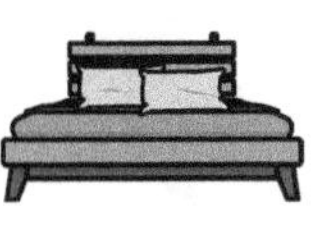 

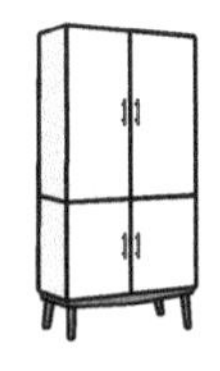  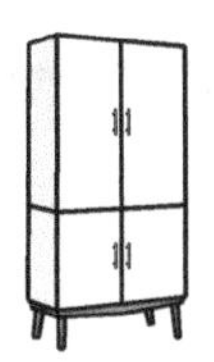  

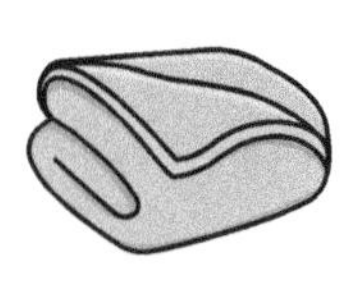  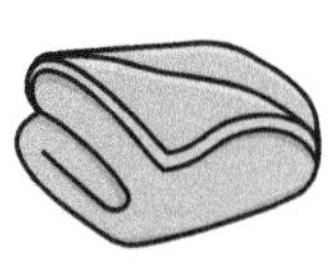  

 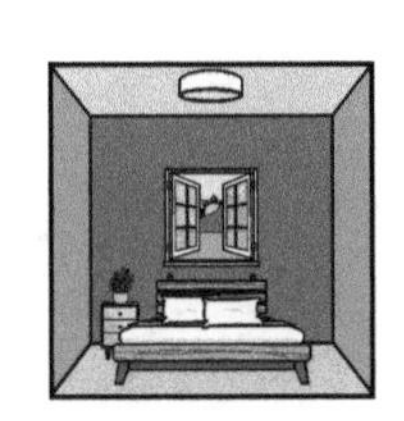 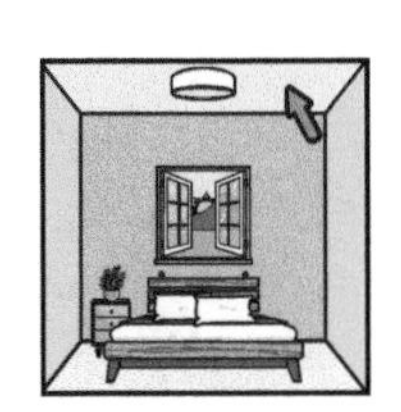  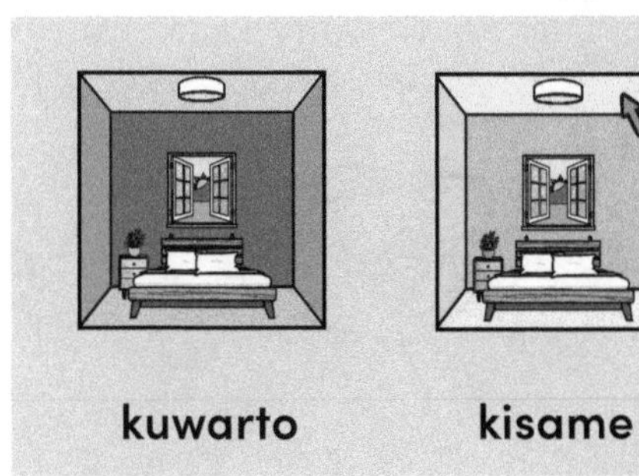

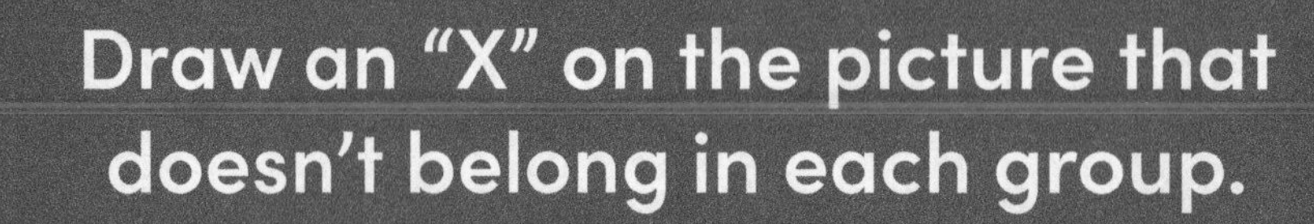

Draw an "X" on the picture that doesn't belong in each group.

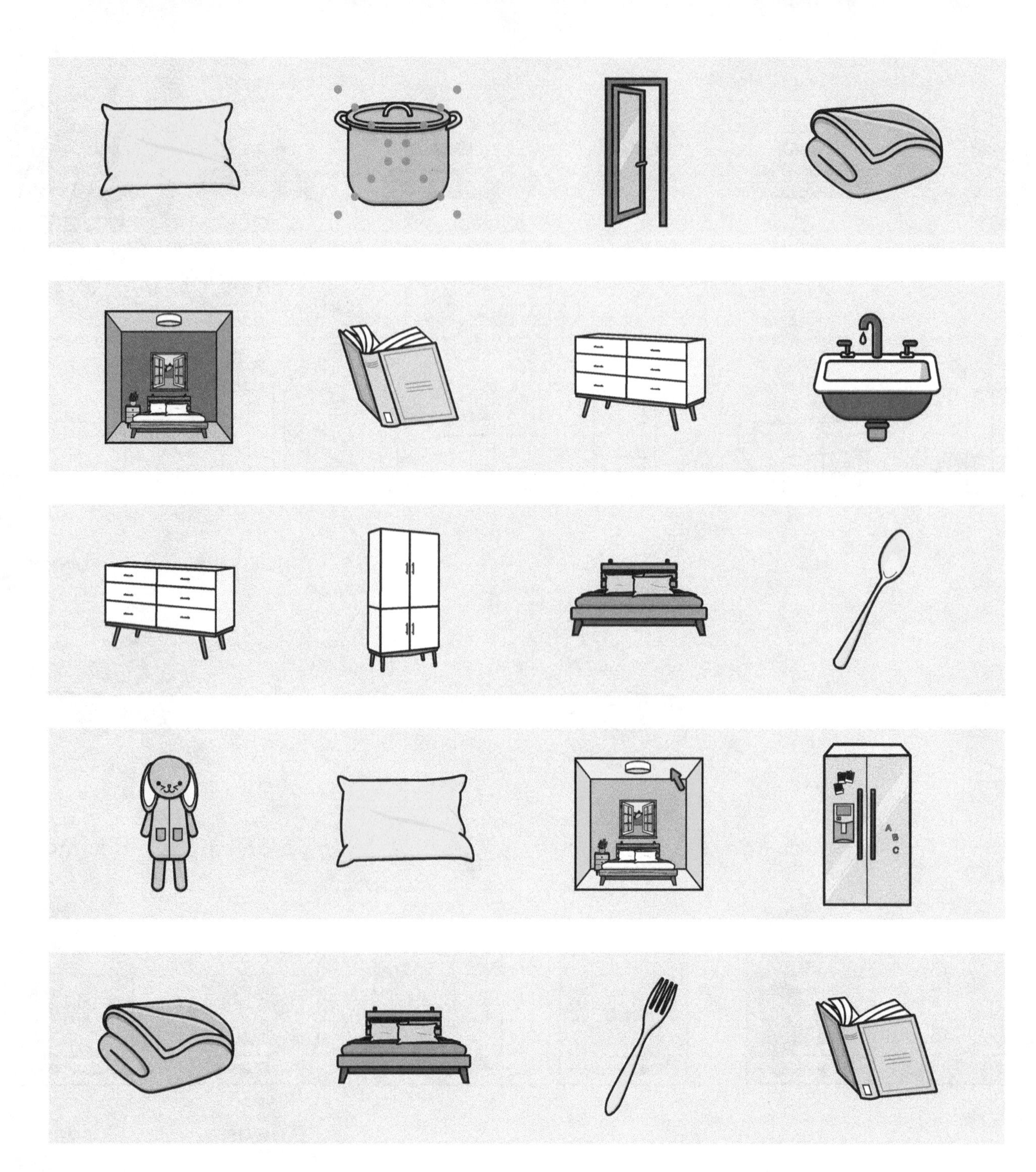

Circle the number of items in each group.

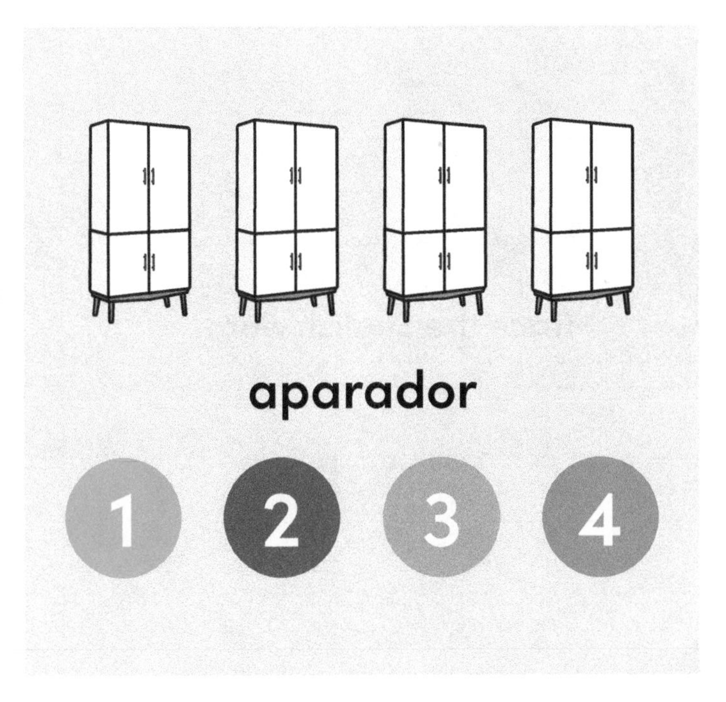

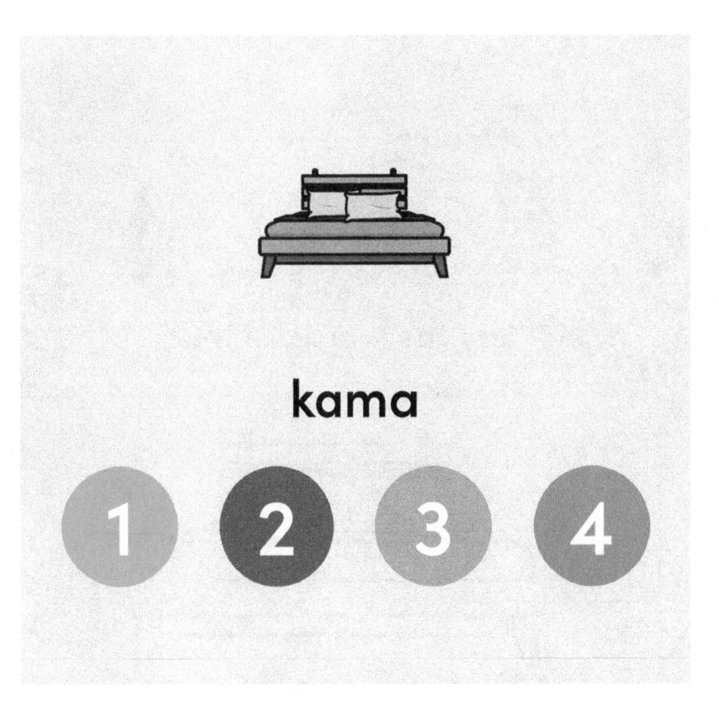

Complete the activity in each box.

kuwarto
(KWAR-to)

Say the word out loud.

Trace the English word.

Color the kuwarto.

Draw a bedroom.

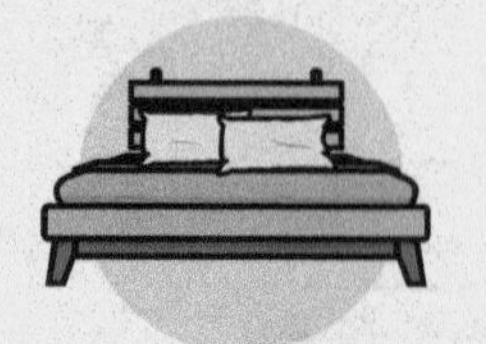

kama
(KA-ma)

Say the word out loud.

Trace the English word.

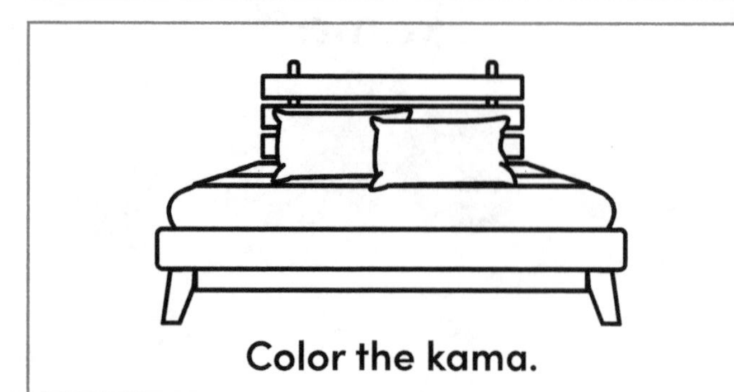

Color the kama.

Draw a bed.

Complete the activity in each box.

aklat
(ak-LAT)

Say the word out loud.

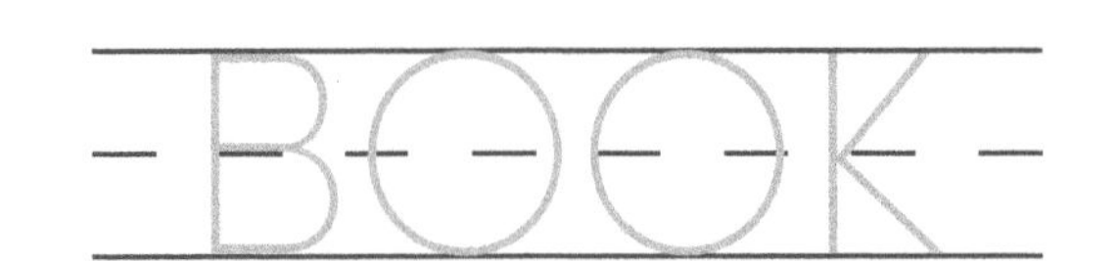

Trace the English word.

Color the aklat.

Draw a book.

unan
(U-nan)

Say the word out loud.

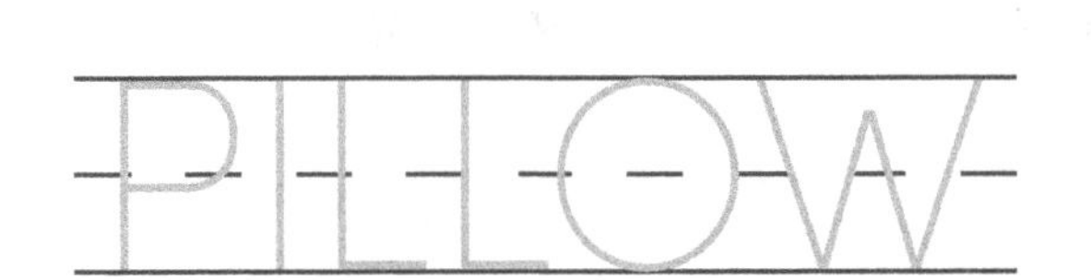

Trace the English word.

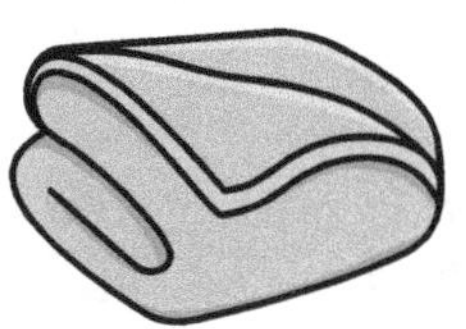

Color the unan.

Draw a pillow.

PART TWO

Kuwarto

Bedroom

Psst! Bookmark this page for easy reference. And remember that Tagalog vowels *A-E-I-O-U* are pronounced *AH-EH-EE-OH-OO.*

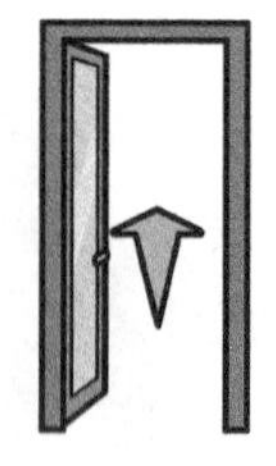

deretso
(de-RE-cho)
straight

gumising
(gu-MI-sing)
wake up

humiga
(hu-mi-GA)
lie down

kaliwa
(ka-li-WA)
left

kanan
(KA-nan)
right

managinip
(ma-na-GI-nip)
to dream

marumi
(ma-ru-MI)
dirty

sa ibabaw
(sa i-BA-baw)
on top

sa ilalim
(sa i-LA-lim)
under

matulog
(ma-TU-log)
to sleep

Say the Tagalog words out loud and trace the missing letters.

GUMISING

MARUMI

DERETSO

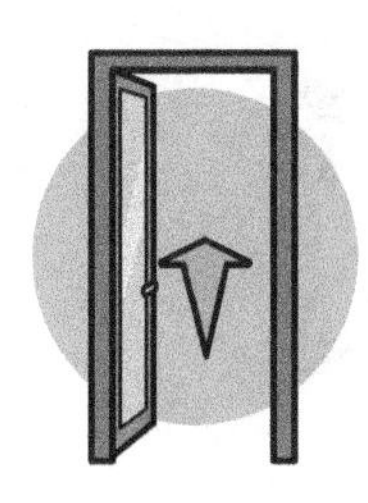

MATULOG

KALIWA

Connect the picture to its matching Tagalog word.

sa ibabaw

humiga

sa ilalim

matulog

managinip

Trace the line to connect the Tagalog word to its matching picture.

deretso

marumi

kaliwa

kanan

gumising

Circle whether the object is
sa ibabaw (on top) or sa ilalim (under).

Circle whether the object is sa ibabaw (on top) or sa ilalim (below).

Draw an "X" on the picture that doesn't belong in each group.

Circle whether the arrow is pointing kaliwa (left), kanan (right), or deretso (straight).

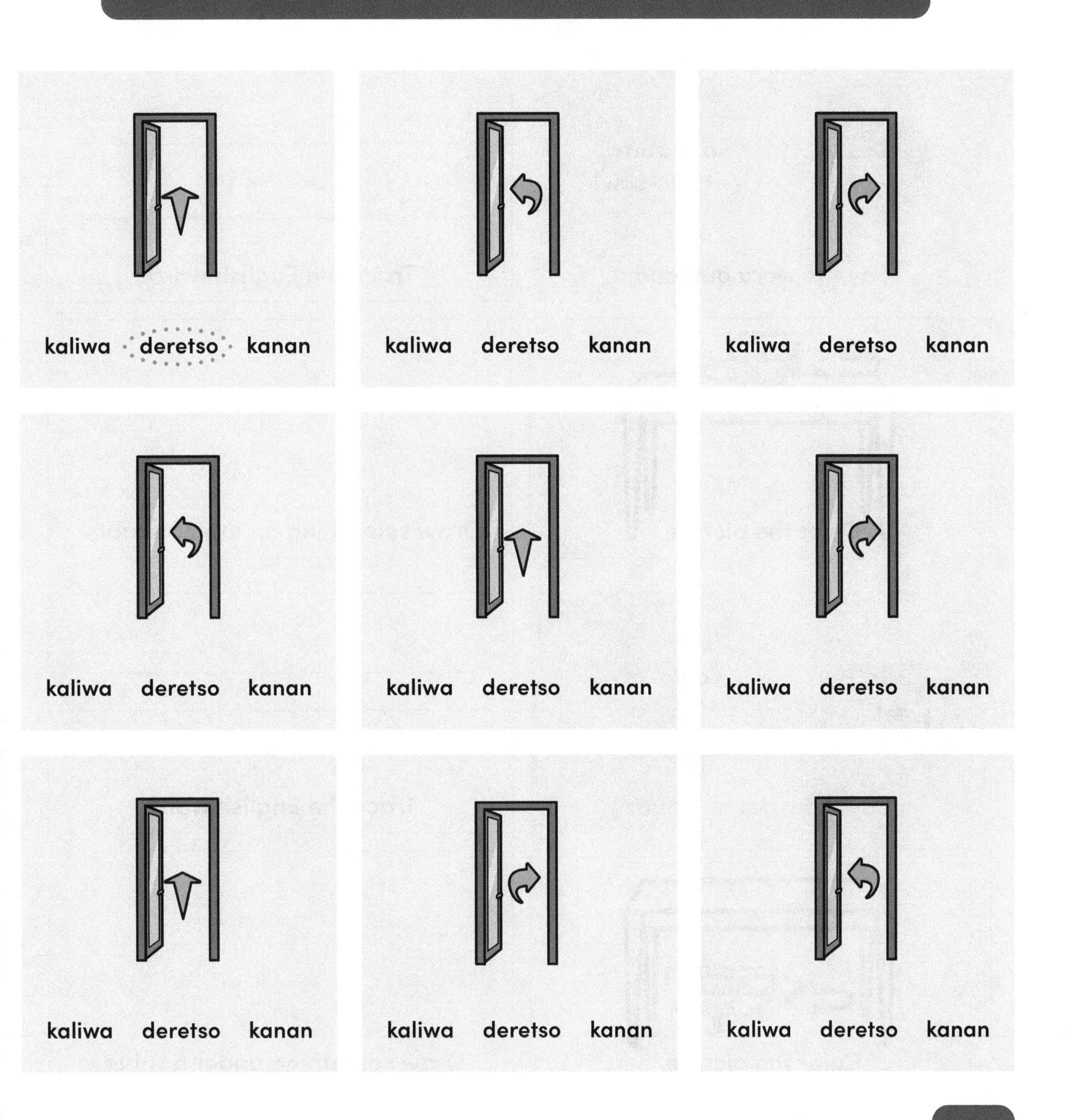

Complete the activity in each box.

sa ibabaw
(sa i-BA-baw)

Say the word out loud.

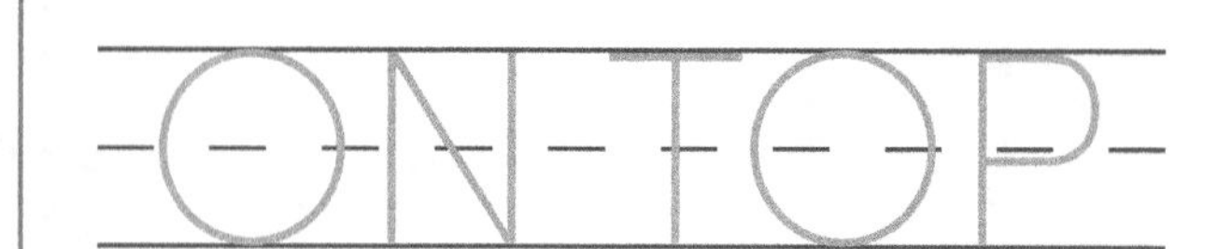

Trace the English word.

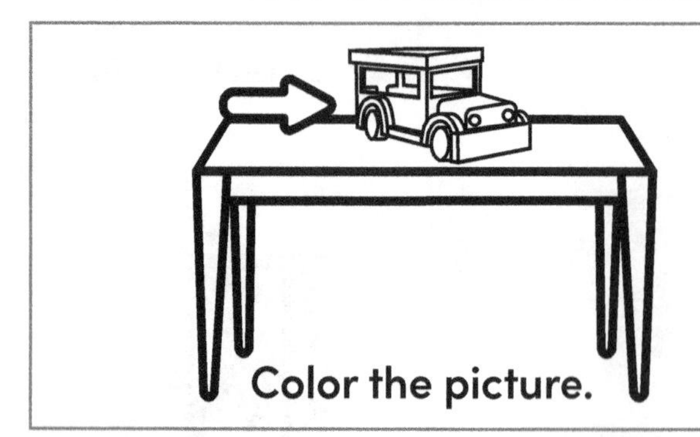

Color the picture.

Draw something on top of a table.

sa ilalim
(sa i-LA-lim)

Say the word out loud.

Trace the English word.

Color the picture.

Draw something under a table.

Complete the activity in each box.

managinip
(ma-na-GI-nip)

Say the word out loud.

Trace the English word.

Color the picture.

Draw a dream.

gumising
(gum-i-sing)

Say the word out loud.

WAKE UP

Trace the English word.

Color the picture.

Draw yourself waking up.

PART ONE

Banyo

Bathroom

Psst! Bookmark this page for easy reference. And remember that Tagalog vowels *A-E-I-O-U* are pronounced *AH-EH-EE-OH-OO*.

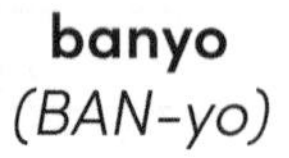

banyo
(BAN-yo)
bathroom

basurahan
(BA-su-ra-han)
trash can

kubeta
(ku-BE-ta)
toilet

lababo
(la-BA-bo)
sink

paliguan
(PA-li-gu-an)
shower

sabon
(sa-BON)
soap

sipilyo
(si-PIL-yo)
toothbrush

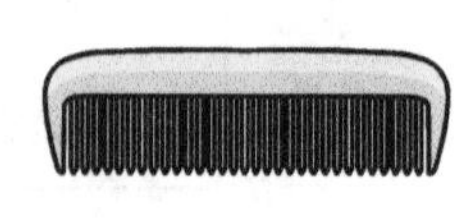

suklay
(suk-LAY)
comb

tabo
(TA-bo)
wash pail

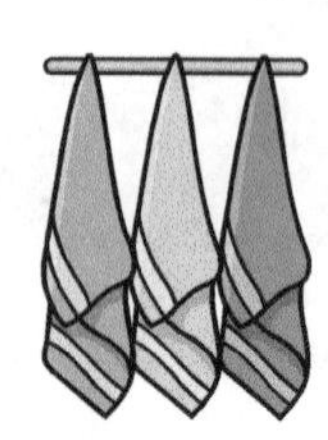

tuwalya
(tu-WAL-ya)
towel

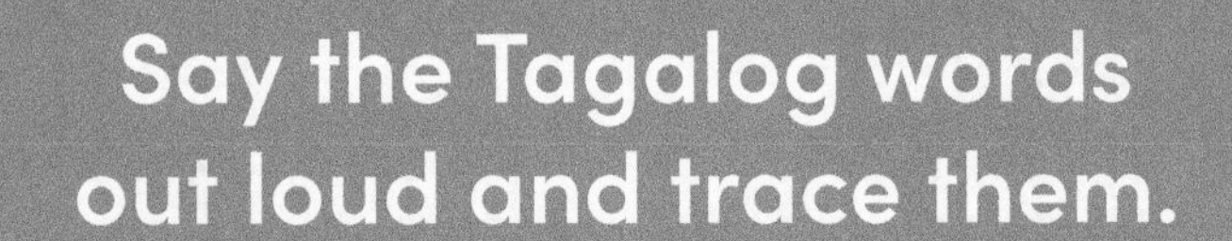

LABABO

KUBETA

SIPILYO

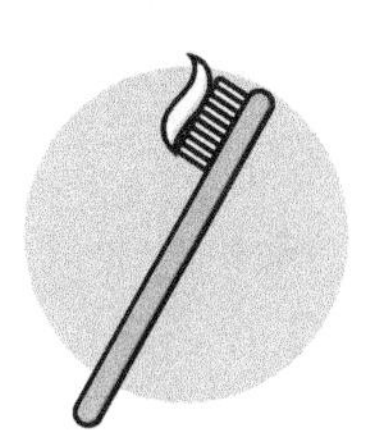

TABO

BASURAHAN

Trace the line to connect the Tagalog word to its matching picture.

paliguan

tuwalya

suklay

kubeta

sabon

Circle the Tagalog word that matches each picture.

banyo suklay  lababo

sink

kubeta tabo sabon

toilet

suklay basurahan sipilyo

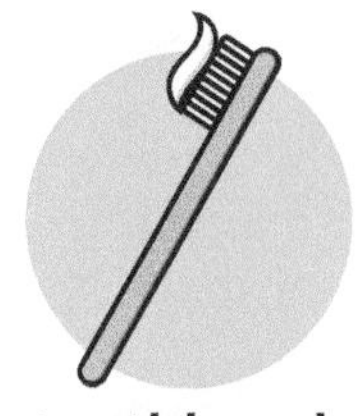
toothbrush

basurahan banyo tuwalya

trash can

paliguan tuwalya suklay

towel

Circle the Tagalog word that matches each picture.

suklay	sabon	banyo	 soap
kubeta	tuwalya	tabo	 wash pail
paliguan	basurahan	sipilyo	 shower
lababo	tabo	banyo	 bathroom
suklay	basurahan	kubeta	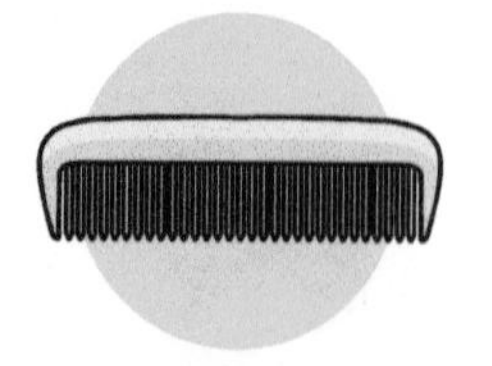 comb

Circle the biggest picture.

Circle the pictures that belong in the banyo (bathroom).

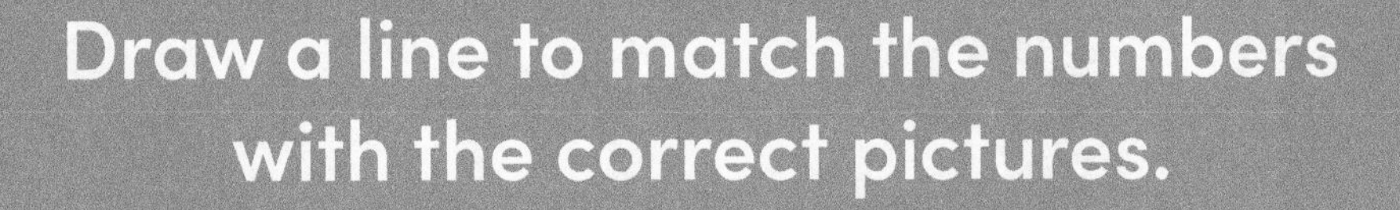

Draw a line to match the numbers with the correct pictures.

2 sipilyo

3 tabo

3 sabon

4 basurahan

2 lababo

Complete the activity in each box.

banyo
(BAN-yo)

Say the word out loud.

Trace the English word.

Color the banyo.

Draw a bathroom.

tabo
(TA-bo)

Say the word out loud.

Trace the English word.

Color the tabo.

Draw a wash pail.

Complete the activity in each box.

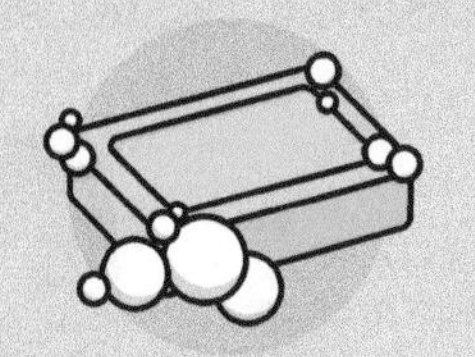

sabon
(sa-BON)

Say the word out loud.

Trace the English word.

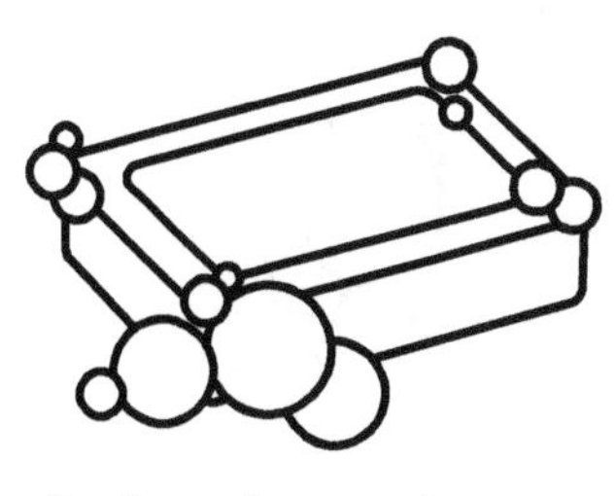

Color the sabon.

Draw soap.

sipilyo
(si-PIL-yo)

Say the word out loud.

Trace the English word.

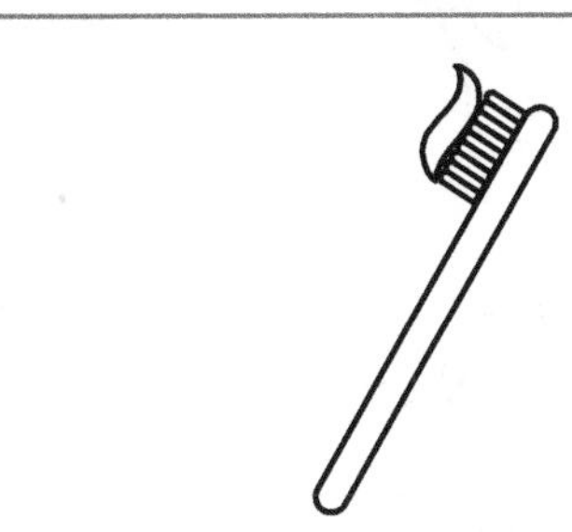

Color the sipilyo.

Draw a toothbrush.

PART TWO

Banyo

Bathroom

Psst! Bookmark this page for easy reference. And remember that Tagalog vowels *A-E-I-O-U* are pronounced *AH-EH-EE-OH-OO.*

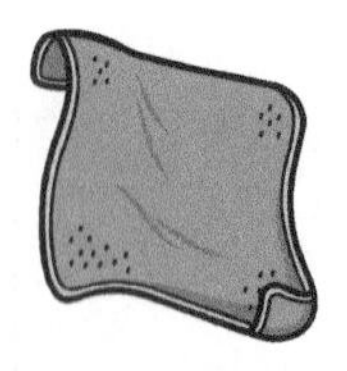

bimpo
(BIM-po)

face towel

maghilamos
(mag-hi-LA-mos)

wash face

maghugas
(mag-HU-gas)

wash

ihi
(I-hi)

pee

maligo
(ma-LI-go)

shower

mabaho
(ma-BA-ho)

stinky

mabango
(ma-ba-NGO)

fragrant

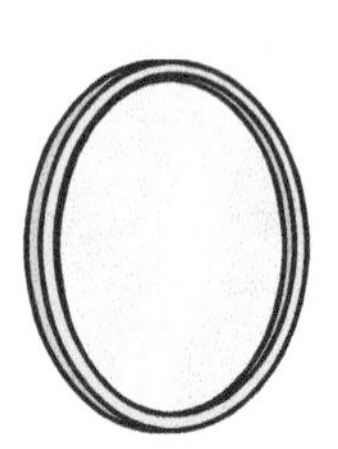

salamin
(sa-la-MIN)

mirror

tae
(TA-e)

poo

tisyu
(TI-shu)

tissue

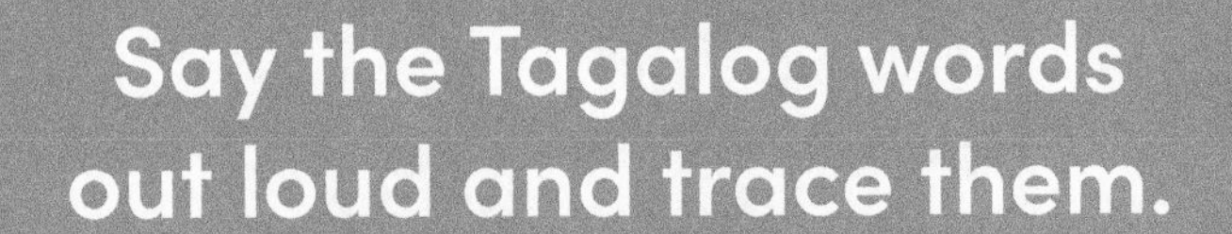

Say the Tagalog words out loud and trace them.

SALAMIN

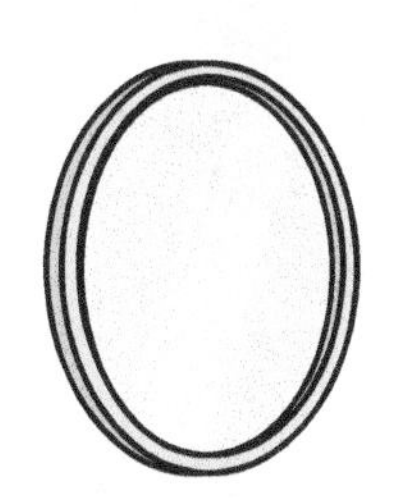

BIMPO

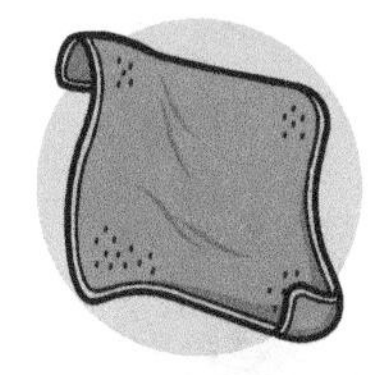

MALIGO

TAE

MABAHO

Trace the line to connect the Tagalog word to its matching picture.

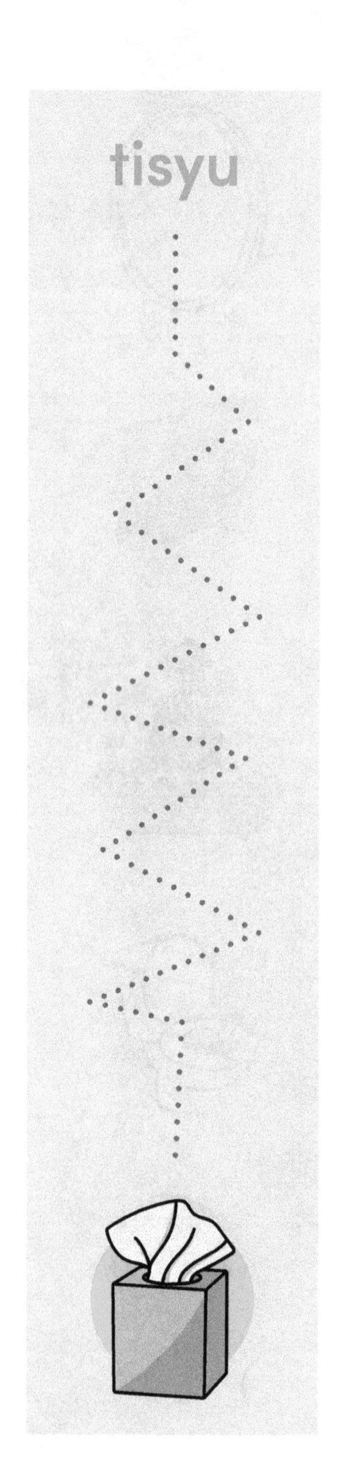

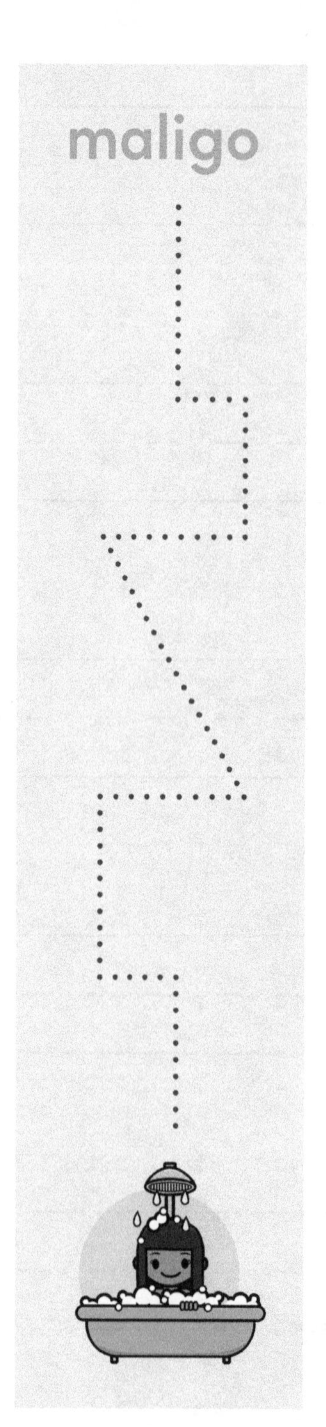

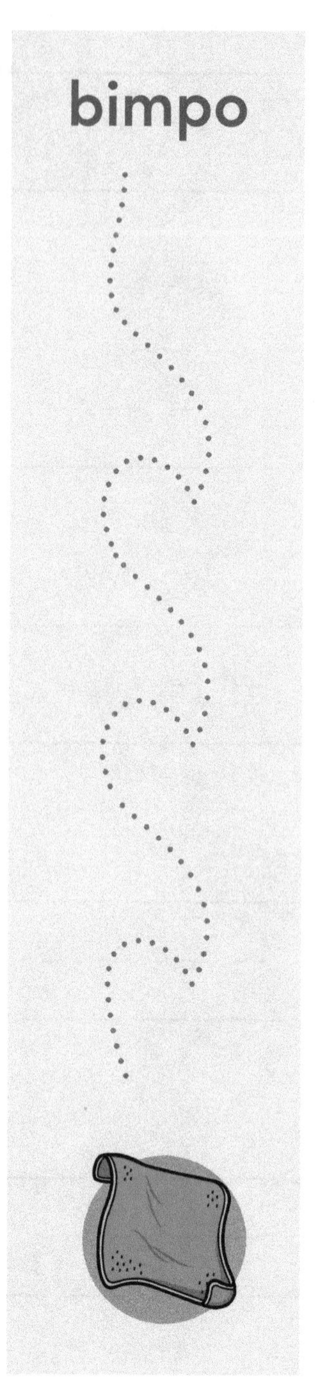

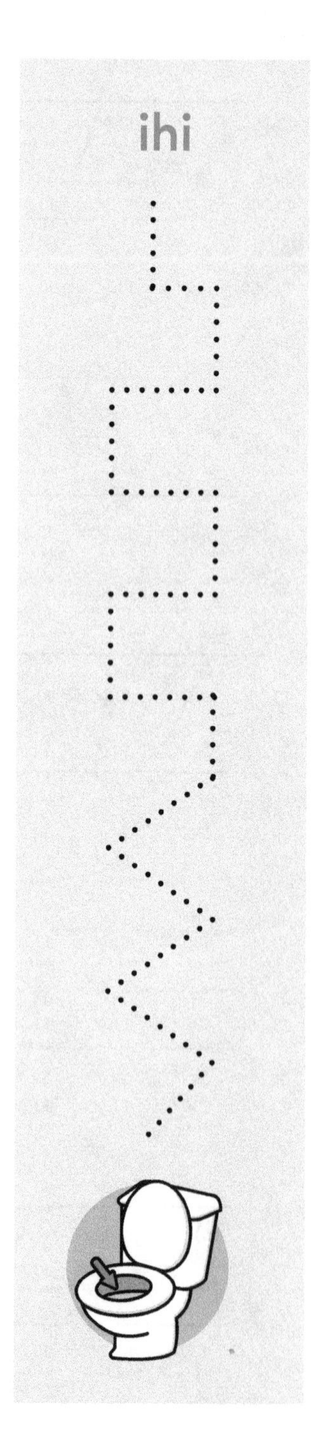

Draw a path to help the person find the bimpo.

Circle the Tagalog word that matches each picture.

tisyu	maligo	maghugas	 wash
tae	ihi	bimpo	 pee
salamin	mabango	tae	 poo
maligo	tisyu	bimpo	 shower
bimpo	maghilamos	mabaho	 wash face

Draw a line to match the numbers with the correct pictures.

4
salamin

2
bimpo

3
tisyu

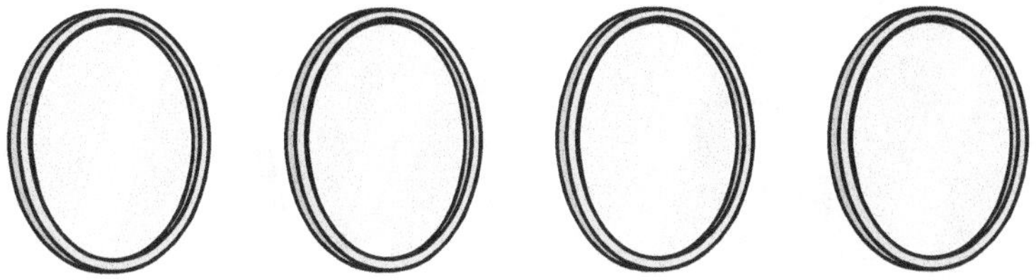

2
ihi

3
tae

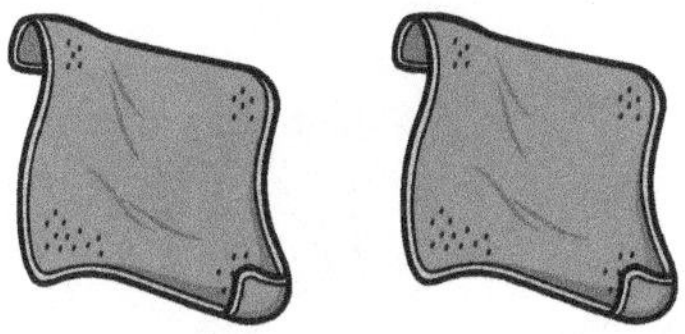

Circle the pictures that belong in the banyo (bathroom).

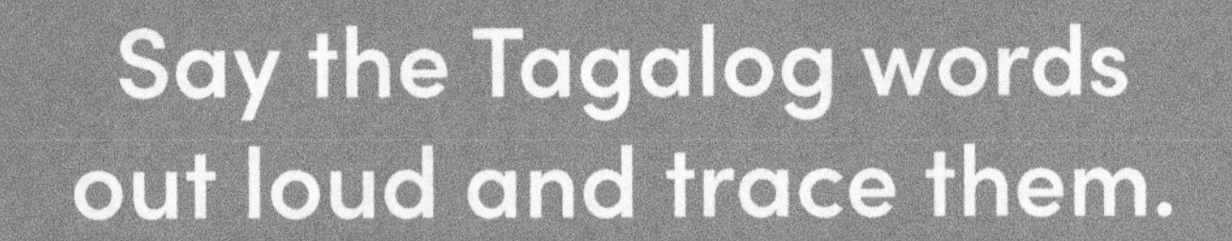

Say the Tagalog words out loud and trace them.

IHI

MABANGO

MABAHO

MALIGO

TISYU

Complete the activity in each box.

maghugas
(mag-HU-gas)

Say the word out loud.

Trace the English word.

Color the picture.

Draw yourself washing your hands.

maligo
(ma-LI-go)

Say the word out loud.

Trace the English word.

Color the picture.

Draw a shower.

Trace the Tagalog word for each room in the bahay (house).

About the Creators

Bien-Elize C. Roque-Nido | Author
Bien-Elize is a passionate Pinay educator and Bay Area native. She has a Master's in Urban Education and 15 years of experience in the field. While she grew up understanding Tagalog as a child, she challenged herself as a teen to practice speaking the language as well. Today, with her background in education, ethnic studies, and language, Bien-Elize dedicates herself to cultivating Filipinx culture in her community. She also loves eating cookies and enJOYing adventures with her hella dope family: Momma, Jun, B'jani, & K'layaan. This book is dedicated to them and Mody. Family hug!

Stephanie Castillo Braulio | Illustrator
Stephanie (Tep) grew up in the Bay Area (mostly Fremont and Union City) before moving to San Diego and L.A. to pursue her undergraduate and graduate education. Her first language was Tagalog, but as she's lost her fluency over the years, she has dedicated herself to relearning. Her goal, of course, is to pass the language on to her children. Tep is a proud second-generation immigrant, wife, mother, friend, educator, and illustrator. She enjoys learning and sharing knowledge with her community, traveling to new places, and trying new foodie spots. She dedicates this book to her SONshines - Wilson, Jameson, and Watson.

McKenly Santos | Designer
McKenly (Ken) was born in Tarlac, Philippines, and moved to San Francisco when he was 8 years old. As a first-generation immigrant, he found it rather challenging to stay in touch with his Filipino roots, so these days, he makes sure to teach his little ones Filipino traditions and languages (he grew up speaking Tagalog and Kapampangan). By day, Ken works as a designer, collaborating with companies like Salesforce, Facebook, Dolby, and Schwab. Meanwhile, outside of work, he loves to explore the outdoors, travel to new places, and try interesting foods with his family. He dedicates this book to his life inspirations, Carmela, Malaya, and Marlo.

Dianne Que | Editor
A Northern California native, Dianne grew up understanding Tagalog but not speaking the language. It was only after living and studying abroad in the Philippines (Tagalog-on-Site, 2003) that she unlocked her fluency. She has since provided Tagalog translation/editing services for documentaries, scripts, books, and other works. Today, she is a Design Operations Director in Tech, with professional roots in non-profit arts and creative agencies. Dianne is dedicated to amplifying Filipinx and BIPOC stories and experiences. She is also a mama, maker, gardener, wanderer, and ice cream eater. She dedicates this work to her family and to Susan, Gayia, and Ged.

CPSIA information can be obtained
at www.ICGtesting.com
Printed in the USA
BVHW020534100323
660102BV00003B/3